NASA SP–230

ECOLOGICAL SURVEYS FROM SPACE

PREPARED FOR THE

Office of Space Science and Applications

UNITED STATES
Scientific and Technical Information Division
OFFICE OF TECHNOLOGY UTILIZATION   1970
NATIONAL AERONAUTICS AND SPACE ADMINISTRATION
Washington, D.C.

FOREWORD

In the 1960's spacecraft became commercial communication tools and began to provide worldwide meteorological data routinely for everyone's use. This monograph points out some of the further feasible uses of spacecraft in the 1970's.

It is a small sampling and condensation of numerous scientific and technical studies of new images and concepts of the Earth that men have acquired by venturing into space. It is intended mainly to call the attention of more specialists, such as geographers, agricultural engineers, foresters, geologists, hydrologists, oceanographers, and cartographers, to the potentialities of ecological surveys from orbiting satellites.

The advantages and disadvantages of remote sensing of various features of the Earth's surface will become more clear, no doubt, in 1972 when NASA's first Earth Resources Technology Satellite (ERTS) is placed in orbit. The photographs reproduced here were taken from aircraft and the Gemini and Apollo vehicles. Additional examples of space photography are available for study in other NASA Special Publications.

CONTENTS

APOLLO 9   AS9-38401

This infrared Ektachrome photo taken March 12, 1969, by the Apollo 9 astronauts shows about 7000 square miles of the Arizona test site. Both natural and cultural resources can be seen here. Phoenix is approximately in the center. Uplands and mountains are distinguishable from agricultural crop and rangeland. Watercourses are prominent across the center. High-resolution aerial photos obtained the same day and "ground truth" data are being used to determine the feasibility of resource inventories from interpretations of space photography such as this.

INTRODUCTION 1

Sophocles found the Earth "rugged" and "all-nourishing." Centuries later Shakespeare called it a "goodly frame." But now many persons fear, like the director of Harvard's Center for Population Studies, that "the 21st century may witness a world of half-starved, depressed human masses, gasping for air, short of sweet water, struggling to avoid one another, living at a degraded subsistence level. . . ."

Such dire views are plausible only because of men's indifference heretofore to the many interactions between the Earth's biosphere and its atmosphere, hydrosphere, and lithosphere. By the recent voyages into space, astronauts have shown people not only how beautiful and small the Earth is but also how similar it is to a spaceship. Both are closed ecological systems in which diligent housekeeping is necessary. Can the "cloud-streaked blue spaceship" that we have found ourselves in be kept habitable for more ages, for more people?

Both the population and the per capita demands on the Earth's resources have risen and seem likely to continue to soar. But so, too, has interest in the retention of a productive environment and the enhancement of the quality of all human life. To attain such objectives, more accurate and frequent inventories of the Earth's resources must be taken than have been compiled in the past. Fortunately, this now can be done both more swiftly and more economically. The whole world's surface can be surveyed as often as necessary, and in a variety of ways, with cameras and other sensing devices on orbiting satellites.

Lines, patterns, and colors in aerial and space photos reveal both what nature and what men have done to the face of the Earth. Land uses traceable to cultural and societal developments usually contrast sharply with phenomena resulting from the natural or physical base. Restricted and regulated by the environment, men have been forced either to adapt themselves to the land or to modify it with machinery and structures. In photos taken from high altitudes, highways appear as networks of fine lines, farm fields produce recognizable patterns, and the areas from which forests have been cleared stand out brightly. Colors are indicative of the vegetation, soil conditions, the depth of water, and many other matters of vital concern to mankind.

This monograph will suggest a few of the possible uses for surveys from spacecraft in seven important disciplines of natural science. Many more uses in more fields of learning are conceivable. Although much of the data presented here will be somewhat elementary, it will be indicative of the potentialities of newly developed vehicles and instrumentation in the study and scientific analysis of the Earth's capabilities. The very abundance of data and information now obtainable makes its storage, interpretation, and dissemination a challenge. Properly processed and utilized, however, this flood of new knowledge can help all mankind safeguard and share the Earth's vast remaining resources.

"Of all man's great enterprises," President Nixon told the United Nations General Assembly on September 18, 1969, "none lends itself more logically or compellingly to international cooperation than the venture into space. . . . We are just beginning to comprehend the benefits that space technology can yield here on Earth."

Experimental Photography

Two of the 17 scientific, engineering, and medical investigations conducted during the manned Gemini flights in 1965 and 1966 were synoptic terrain and weather photography experiments. The results clearly established the value of such photography in nearly all occupations concerned with the Earth. In February 1967, the National Aeronautics and Space Administration contracted with the Geodesy Intelligence and Mapping Research and Development Agency (GIMRADA) of the U.S. Army Corps of

Engineers to produce a report entitled *Earth Resources Surveys from Spacecraft*. Two illustrated volumes resulted from the work of GIMRADA and associated specialists representing business, academic, and other Government groups; and much of the information in this monograph was assembled in the course of that effort.

The Gemini flights were preparatory for the Apollo missions to the Moon. Arrangements were made on short notice for additional Earth photography by the Apollo 9 astronauts in March 1968 as a result of the widespread recognition of the potential significance of the Gemini photography. The Apollo 9 scientific experiment no. 065 (abbreviated as SO–65) was performed under the auspices of NASA's Earth Resources Survey Program in cooperation with the U.S. Department of Agriculture, Department of the Interior, Environmental Science Services Administration, Naval Oceanographic Office, and other interested agencies, firms, and institutions. This experiment, according to Prof. Robert N. Colwell of the University of California at Berkeley, "could easily prove to be the most important photographic experiment in history."

The frontispiece and some of the other color photographs presented here are indicative of the pictures that Astronauts James McDivitt, David Scott, and Russell Schweickart obtained. They had a four-camera system on Apollo 9 with which to photograph test sites designated beforehand in the United States. Each camera had a different combination of photographic film and filter, but all four were triggered simultaneously to show the same area. The test sites were in the Imperial Valley of California, near Phoenix in Arizona, the Tucson-Willcox-Fort Huachuca triangle in Arizona, and near Vicksburg, Miss. Aircraft at altitudes ranging from a few hundred feet to about 70 000 ft photographed portions of these sites almost simultaneously with the spacecraft, and carried "optical mechanical scanners" to sense the energy reflected from the Earth's surface in various wavelength bands of the electromagnetic spectrum. In addition, both terrestrial photographs and on-the-ground measurements were made to ascertain the radiant energy emanating at the time from representative Earth resource features in some parts of the test sites.

The energy sensed in aerial and space photography is reflected solar energy, and the spectrum used for such photography is comprised of wavelengths that range from about 400 to 900 millimicrons. Shorter wavelengths are scattered excessively by haze, and longer wavelengths are seldom used because of the difficulty of producing thermostable photographic emulsions that are sufficiently fine grained.

The Selection of Wavelengths

The 400- to 900-millimicron range of wavelengths of light embraces all colors of the visible spectrum (violet, indigo, blue, green, yellow, orange, and red), together with wavelengths just a little longer than the visible red, known as the near infrared. It is often helpful to consider this 400- to 900-millimicron range as one composed of four "bands," three of which are in the visible and one in the infrared region. The three visible bands correspond to the three primary colors: blue, green, and red. With only moderate oversimplification, the wavelengths embraced by the four bands can be considered to be:

Band	Wavelength range, millimicrons
Blue	400 to 500
Green	500 to 600
Red	600 to 700
Infrared	700 to 900

An aerial or space photo can be taken in any one of these bands by (1) using a film sensitive to energy in that band and (2) employing a filter that transmits energy in that band but excludes energy of other wavelengths to which the film is sensitive.

The choice of a band to use for an aerial or space photo of the Earth depends largely on two factors: the degree to which the objects to be recorded reflect energy from each of the four bands, and the extent to which haze particles in the atmosphere scatter radiant energy from each band.

The more energy an object reflects to the camera in any given wavelength band, the brighter the image of that object will be on the positive print when a picture is taken in that band (i.e., the lighter its photographic tone becomes). Because the amount of energy reflected in a given band tends to be a function of the type of object, the tones obtained object by object when photographing in that band are important aids to the identification of objects.

Two types of objects may have virtually the same reflectivity in one of the four bands, but quite different reflectivities in some other band. Each type of object, in other words, tends to exhibit a unique "tone signature" in multiband photography, and this signature is often of great value in recognizing an object.

The shape and texture of an object can also help a person identify it. Other factors being equal, however, the higher the altitude from which a photo of the Earth's surface is taken, the less detail can be seen in an object's shape and texture. The photographic interpreter (or image-analyzing machine) must place greater reliance on the tone signature when the shape and texture are indistinct.

For haze particles of the size commonly encountered in the Earth's atmosphere, energy scattering is in conformity with Rayleigh's law; i.e., inversely proportional to the fourth power of the wavelength of the energy. Because scattering causes a loss of image sharpness, the shortest of the four wavelength bands (the blue band) is of little value when aerial or space photographs are taken of the Earth's surface. This band, consequently, was not recommended for use in the SO–65 multispectral photographic experiment on the Apollo 9 flight in 1969.

Table 1 provides three authoritative expressions of the wavelength range encompassed by each of the four bands discussed here. Table 2 suggests optimum bands for various studies.

TABLE 1   METHODS OF EXPRESSING WAVELENGTH RANGE

Terms used to describe the band	Wavelength range, millimicrons		
	As taught in elementary physics	As flown on Apollo 9 (SO–65)	As proposed for ERTS [a]
Blue	400 to 500		
Green	500 to 600	480 to 620	475 to 575
Red	600 to 700	590 to 720	580 to 680
Infrared (near infrared)	700 to 900	720 to 900	690 to 830

[a] Earth Resources Technology Satellite.

TABLE 2   OPTIMUM WAVELENGTH BAND FOR TYPE OF PHOTO IDENTIFICATION TO BE MADE

Photo identification to be made	Optimum wavelength band			
	Blue	Green	Red	Infrared
Presence or absence of vegetation				X
Differentiating conifers from broadleaf vegetation				X
Identifying individual species of plants		X	X	X
Detecting earliest evidence of loss of vigor in vegetation				X
Identifying type of agent that is causing the loss of vigor		X	X	
Determining the exact channel of a meandering stream				X
Obtaining maximum underwater detail (varies with turbidity)		X	X	
Discerning maximum detail in shaded areas on low-altitude photos only	X			

Restoration of Harmony

Scholars concerned with the biosphere hope to develop and test theories that would explain the creation, maintenance, and occasional destruction of various ecosystems. Such theories might help them note which systems are more fragile than others, evaluate the sometimes beneficial as well as damaging effects of fires and landslides, and offer better guidance to managers of Earth resources.

Chlorophyll green is an observable characteristic of many ecosystems that is closely related to the Earth's productivity. Possibly its intensity could be measured on a gray scale, and possibly a combination of sensors could be developed that would be helpful in determining how the whole biomass is distributed over the Earth's surface. Clearly, a great deal of groundwork must be done to assure the accuracy of ecological surveys from spacecraft. Test sites typical of and centered in each of the world's major ecosystems, as well as in transition zones such as those between tropical forests and savannas, may be needed.

The Earth has nourished thousands of generations of many forms of life, but no creature ever saw more than a small fraction of the Earth until our time. Seeing the world as a whole will not suffice to solve mankind's problems. Ecological surveys from spacecraft, nevertheless, can illuminate the obstacles to restoring productive harmony between man and nature.

It is not easy for a novice to extract useful information from photographs taken from spacecraft, but qualified persons can do so with the proper tools. To succeed in this task (1) there must be a clear understanding of the specific kinds of inventory data needed for the intelligent management of our natural resources, (2) the imagery obtained from orbit must be of suitable quality for the extraction of the desired data, (3) the persons performing the work must be properly trained, (4) the equipment used to view, measure, and interpret the imagery must be of suitable quality, and (5) the methods and techniques of the image analyst must enable him to obtain the desired information efficiently and accurately. Revolutionary new tools are needed because the present use of resources has rendered conventional aerial surveys inadequate.

Much of the information presented in this chapter was drawn from reports by Prof. Robert N. Colwell and his associates at the University of California, Berkeley.

GEOGRAPHY 2

Geography once meant literally "to write about the Earth." Geographers complain now that scientists in related disciplines have left them very little to inventory. We still rely primarily upon the geographer, however, to bring each scientist's findings about the Earth into the proper regional and global perspective, and more often than not the geographers still participate in the inventory-taking task.

The feasibility of developing and managing the Earth's natural riches more efficiently, once they have been inventoried, will be affected by the cultural context in which such resources are found. Here, too, the geographers can render a distinct service to mankind by providing cultural maps and analyses that will clarify the issues. These are certainly not trivial services that the geographer can render to managers of the Earth's resources.

Nile Delta Settlements

Figure 1 is a picture showing parts of the United Arab Republic, Jordan, Saudi Arabia, Iraq, and Israel. It was taken with a handheld camera and indicates what vast areas can be observed under relatively uniform lighting, at a single point in time, from a spacecraft. Some of the land features of interest are annotated on the reproduction of the view here. Such a photo reduces the need for crisscrossing a region with aircraft and tediously preparing mosaics to perceive the relationships of various features.

Figure 2 is a less oblique view of a smaller area, obtained similarly, and figure 3 is a map showing cultural elements of this area that was compiled by study of the space photography. The dark blue-green triangle is the great Nile Delta, and the river valley extends south from it. Another narrow, greenish arm extending to the right (east) is the Ismailia Canal. Tan areas around the irrigated region are barren desert.

Within the irrigated area, small, irregular, rectilinear forms ranging in color from pale to dark blue green represent the field pattern. Note the smaller size and irregular orientation of the fields near the center of the delta. Fields showing the darkest shades may be flooded. Water in such fields would be still and would have lost its load of silt, thereby increasing the absorption of solar radiation and reducing its reflectivity. This is also true of the cutoff distributary, Bahr El Faraoniya, which appears as a dark, irregular line near the central part of the left half of the delta. This cutoff is filled by seepage and carries little load. Its reflectivity is much less than that of canals and the river.

Note the larger, rectangular fields on the desert margins of the delta (particularly south of the Ismailia Canal). These fields represent recent attempts to reclaim desertland and show the impact of modern surveying, irrigation techniques, and greater capitalization by their larger size and regular orientation at right angles to the desert margin.

Buff-colored areas within the irrigated zone are human settlements. Cairo and its suburbs appear as a large buff patch near the east side of the southern tip of the inverted delta of irrigated land. A sequence of photos over several years would show a definite change in the city's size and shape. Comparisons of this photo with earlier maps of Cairo clearly indicate an increase in settlement size, but distortion in the photo and unreliable map coverage preclude exact measurements at this time.

The buff-colored band leading southwest from Cairo to the margin of the western desert is the El Giza Road. The Great Pyramids are on the desert margin just to the south of the west end of this road, but are invisible because of the high reflectivity of the desert surface. Few cultural features are discernible on the desert, but more careful camera exposures insuring greater contrast on the bright surfaces might disclose roads and airports. The clearly defined and regular spacing of small and large settlements at the foci of canals and roads in the delta area indicates that such photos can be an important tool in the analysis of settlement patterns.

The Nile River and its distributaries within the delta appear as sinuous buff-colored ribbons. The main stream lies against the east (right) side of the valley to the south. The Rosetta Distributary is seen winding along the west margin of the delta, while the Damietta Distributary roughly bisects the irrigated area. Meanders and islands are everywhere in evidence. The major canal system appears as a series of straight, buff-colored lines radiating outward from settlement nodes. Such straight-line segments are nearly always canals rather than roads. The latter are narrower and not easily visible. Close observation reveals a fine network of lines that are small canals leading water to field areas. A number of canal junctions can also be identified.

Irregular, mottled areas of varying size are sand blowouts. These are shown by a striped pattern on the map in figure 3. Their cloudlike forms are deceptive, but the absence of shadows shows they are topographic features. Distinction between these and settlements is further enhanced by the lack of canal orientation to sandy areas (unlike the appearance of urban sites as nodes on canal networks).

The regularity of the settlement pattern in the delta photo suggests the possibility of research concerning Christaller's and other location models by the use of this type of photo. A further basic step in this type of research would be to assign population values to all identifiable settlements. This might make it possible to predict the population of settlements by correlation with the size of the settled area as shown on satellite photos, and prediction of a settlement's size by its location within the network of settlements.

Land and Water Use

A series of photographs over a year or several years would allow analysis of farming patterns, crop conditions (when compared with agricultural census reports), the impact of floods and droughts, expansion of urban areas at the expense of agricultural land (a significant portion of the Nile Delta is devoted to nonagricultural land use), and changes in transportation facilities and irrigation systems.

More careful camera exposures might reveal cultural features of interest in desert areas. Archeological sites would certainly become evident with proper imagery.

Figure 4 is another Gemini picture of northern Africa. This is part of Tripolitania, and the port of Tripoli is in the upper center where a tiny hook extends into the blue Mediterranean. A photograph on this scale is primarily useful to illustrate large landforms and physiographic units. These include a low coast with bright clean sand and dunes, which is visible here as a small, nearly white, discontinuous strip. Below this in the photo is a belt of oases and gardens (delineated in fig. 5). Here from 10 to 16 in. of precipitation during the winter and a good supply of ground water enable the people to grow tree crops (dates, citrus fruits, olives, figs, almonds), cereals, vegetables, grapevine peanuts, and tobacco. Sand dunes, mostly bare of vegetation, interrupt these oases, and farther inland one sees the open plain of Jefara. It consists of sandy Quaternary deposits and has a semiarid climate and a steppe vegetation. There is less rainfall and ground water there, and the dominant agricultural activities are grazing sheep, goats, cattle, camels, etc., and dry farming.

To the south the plain of Jefara is framed by a big semicircle where the Jebel, a mountain area, rises out of the plain to an elevation of 2000 to 3000 ft. It is part of the limb of a vast dome-shaped anticline of Cretaceous and Jurassic limestones, dolomites, sandstones, etc., with a sharp escarpment to the north and a plateau falling slowly to the southeast (in the lower right corner). Here there are springs that support human settlements, and cultivation of olives and field crops alternates with grazing of sheep and goats. Wadis stretch from the escarpment into the plain. Bare streambeds are visible on the piedmont but disappear in the plain. The striking rectangular area in the center is a recent development of olive cultivation (combined with other crops) started in the late 1930's by the Italians. The land is divided into a rectangular road pattern and scattered homesteads have been established thereabouts; the plain shows a similar pattern of systematically distributed wells.

Figure 6 is another example of Gemini photography that reveals a great deal about the land use and hydrology of an agricultural region. This picture shows about 10 000 square miles of the western end of the Gulf Coastal Plain of the United States between Laredo and Uvalde, Tex. Located south of the Balcones Escarpment, this area includes the upper part of a gently falling coastal plain, an undulated surface of Tertiary (especially Eocene) deposits.

Clouds partly cover the land in the west along the Rio Grande. Several streams and creeks are cut in the

(*Continued on page 12*)

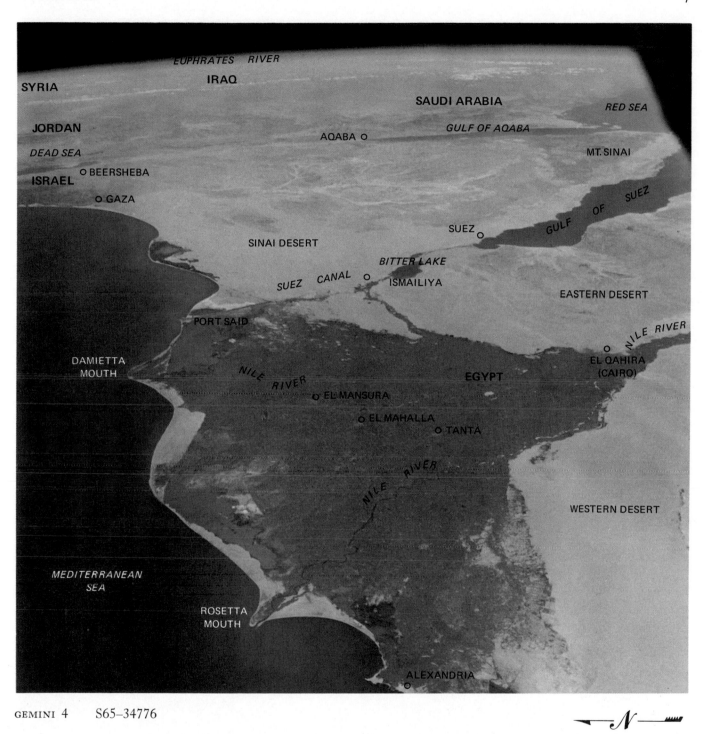

GEMINI 4   S65–34776

FIGURE 1   This Gemini picture was taken with a 70-mm Hasselblad Model C and an 80-mm Zeiss planar lens.

GEMINI 5   S65–45778

FIGURE 2   The Nile Valley extends south from the great delta shown here. Cairo is in the
lower center.

APPROXIMATE

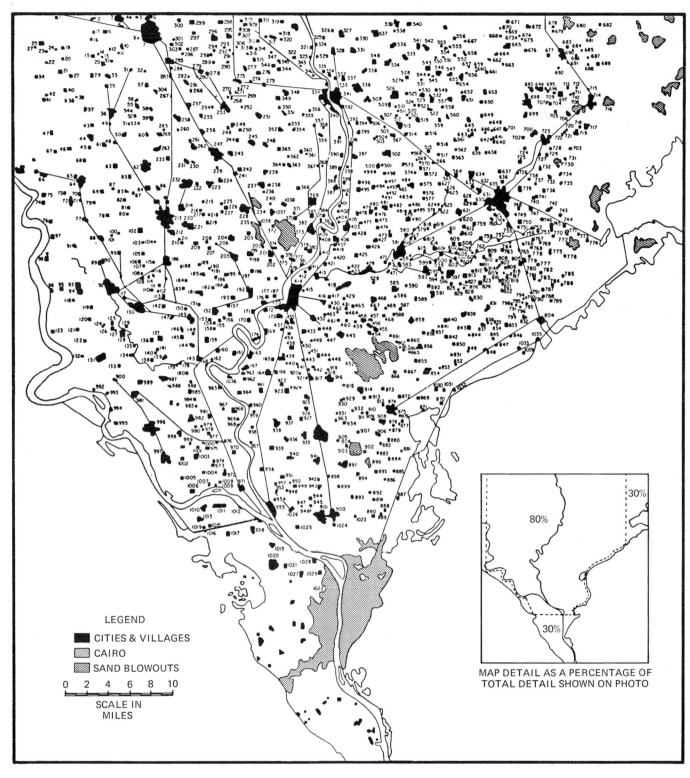

LEGEND

■ CITIES & VILLAGES

▨ CAIRO

▨ SAND BLOWOUTS

0 2 4 6 8 10

SCALE IN
MILES

MAP DETAIL AS A PERCENTAGE OF
TOTAL DETAIL SHOWN ON PHOTO

80%

30%

30%

MAP COMPILED BY JOHN KOLARS AND GEORGE ASPBURY

FIGURE 3   Cultural elements discernible in figure 2 include many cities, villages, and sand blowouts.

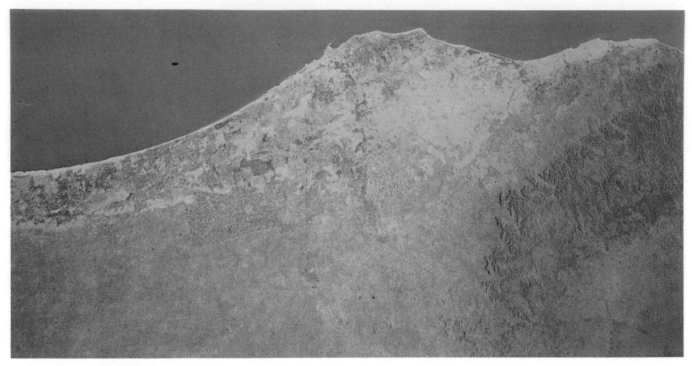

GEMINI 5   S65–45513
FIGURE 4   The Mediterranean coast of Africa around Tripoli. Approximate scale along shore: 1:785 000.

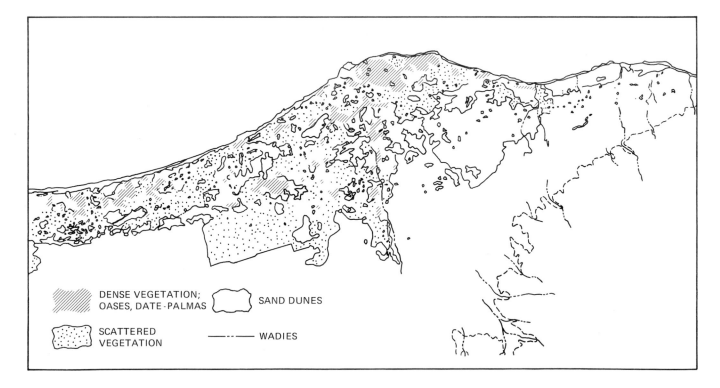

DENSE VEGETATION;
OASES, DATE-PALMAS   SAND DUNES

SCATTERED
VEGETATION   ———·——— WADIES

FIGURE 5   Boundaries of agricultural land use and landforms in northern Libya (as seen in fig. 4).

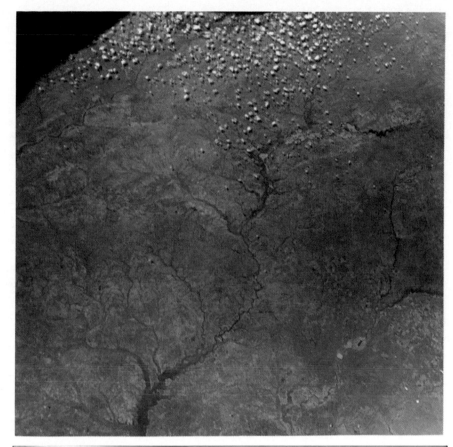

FIGURE 6
A Gemini photo of Texas
brush country that is also known
as a "winter garden" when
irrigated.

GEMINI 5
S65–45782

Water divide, Rio Grande
and Nueces Rivers   a

Soil formation, Duval series   b

Vegetation and wet soil   c

Irrigated areas   d

Field pattern orientation   e ✕

plain, having formed shallow, broad valleys. This is mainly the drainage basin of the Nueces River, which receives tributaries from the west and the south, such as Turkey and Comanche Creek near Crystal City, San Rogue Creek, Las Raices Creek, Los Alamos Creek, San Casimiro Creek, Black Creek, etc., and Espio Creek from the north. The Frio River, with its main tributaries Leona River, Jahuey Creek, and San Miguel Creek, joins the Nueces farther downstream.

The water divide (a) is not very obvious or easy to establish. A more conspicuous feature is the reddish soil formation of the Duval series (b) that crosses through the center of the picture in a large belt from south to north between the light-gray soils of the Maverick series in the west and the brown-colored soils of the Victoria series in the east. It is obvious that the terrain conditions of the Nueces Valley floor are different (drier and supporting less vegetation) in the area of the Duval soils. The color photography brings out these soil differences much better than the black and white.

The land has a semihumid climate with from 20 to 25 in. of precipitation. It is known as brushland because of its subtropical vegetation of small trees (mesquite), thorny shrubs, cactus, weeds, and short grass, called mesquite-chaparral. The valley floors have different water conditions and denser vegetation, including different trees such as pecan, elm, oak, etc. This green vegetation in combination with the wet soil (c), sometimes even swampy ground as in the lower Nueces Valley, makes the dendritic drainage pattern very evident in the photograph.

Ranching of cattle, goats, and sheep is the main use of this brush country. But the same region has also another name, the "winter garden," where all kinds of vegetables and fruits are produced. If the land can be irrigated, excellent harvests in late winter and spring can be expected. The irrigation water (d) comes mainly from wells but also from stream reservoirs. The orientation of the field patterns (e) around a town differs from place to place, and shows that Texas has no single standard type of land survey.

Descriptions of space photography in this chapter were drawn from the work of Harold Haefner, University of California, Los Angeles; and Waldo Toblar, John Kolars, and George Aspbury, University of Michigan.

AGRICULTURE 3

It is especially helpful to observe croplands sequentially from spacecraft because of the dramatic changes that occur in them. The managers of cultivated vegetational resources need to know such things about the foods and fibers growing in the world's major agricultural basins as (1) the type of crop in each field, (2) the size of the field, (3) the vigor of the crop, (4) the identity of any damaging agents, and (5) the probable yield per unit of area. Given such information, one can arrive at regional and global inventories and yield forecasts by simple mathematics. Steps then can be taken to keep the supply of essential foods and fibers in balance with the demand for them.

Both agriculturists and wildland managers also find it helpful to know such terrain characteristics for each area as the slope, aspect, and soil depth, texture, chemical composition, moisture content, and susceptibility to erosion. Conservation requires, too, that men know the state of deterioration brought about by overgrazing, overcropping, repeated burning, erosion, or mineral depletion in each of many great areas.

Several Decades' Experience

Agricultural agencies in the United States have used aerial photography extensively since the early 1930's. Acreage-control staffs have located and measured fields this way, and such photography also has been a means of collecting crop-forecast data. Single aerial photographs, however, provide very little information, and time is required to interpret and collect it. The deadlines for crop reporting do not permit many days to elapse between the gathering of data and the reporting because conditions can change markedly in a short time.

The use of simultaneous multispectral photography, color photography, multichannel optical mechanical scanners, and radar-type imaging systems to gather data on ag-

ricultural crops has heightened interest in the application of modern aerial sensing techniques to gathering crop census data. Preliminary studies indicate that multispectral imagery collected over different crop types in the photographic and infrared regions of the electromagnetic spectrum may show marked differences in tone on the resulting photographs. These studies imply that crop species may be differentiated by the tone responses on imagery generated by multispectral cameras and sensors. Equipment for either direct recording of energy returns from crops in electronic form on magnetic tape, or conversion of tones on photographs into electronic signals on magnetic tape, has made it possible to consider the use of computers in analyzing data.

Feasibility studies of multispectral remote sensing of agricultural areas from aircraft and the planning of cameras and other sensing devices for experiments to be conducted from spacecraft have been underway in a project sponsored jointly by NASA and the Department of Agriculture, at the Universities of Michigan and California, at Purdue University, and at the USDA Soil and Water Laboratory at Weslaco, Tex. The studies have included the design and use of special spectrophotometers and radiometers that will measure reflectance and emission from areas of cropland several feet square at a height of 50 ft above the crop. These devices will permit measurements of energy returns from the same orientation as the airborne sensors—from above. This is considered important because the "geometry" of crops growing in drill rows or in wider rows makes a big difference in the amount of soil that is exposed to the airborne sensors.

Plants and soils have quite different energy-return values in a number of regions of the spectrum. Crop plants can also be expected to have different values as the plants grow, flower, fruit, and mature. Fields of maize, sorghum, wheat, and oats, for example, change in energy reflectance and emission as the plants produce tassels or heads. Using the ground-based spectrophotometer and radiometer, spectral signatures of crops may be studied and compared at intervals during the growing season with spectral signatures recorded by an array of sensors in aircraft flying at variable heights. If, at any given time in crop plant development, a good correlation in measurements between the ground instruments and aircraft sensors flown at low and high altitudes can be established, we will have available a low-cost ground method of predicting results with aircraft. Such methods are essential to study of the wide variability of crops and soils and conditions of crop disease, weed infestation, etc.

Figure 7 shows how readily two different grain crops can be distinguished with a multilens camera. Figure 8 is an example of aerial photography that reveals crop vigor, growth, and soil salinity.

Both agriculturists and hydrologists are concerned with the salt content of water. Unfortunately, no practical means of recording salinity directly with a remote sensor has been found. But certain types of vegetation require salt water, or other brackish water, whereas most plants require fresh water. When photographed from aloft in infrared, the plants that grow in brackish water are bright red, and those that require fresh water are pink, as shown in figure 9. Signatures similar to these could be recognized in space photos as well as in aerial views because infrared waves are not basically affected by the atmosphere.

From the data that have become available from spacecraft sensing (photographs, low-resolution infrared strip maps, etc.), it appears that surveys from space can supplement and enhance the value of aircraft sensing. The principal problems to be solved appear to be improved resolution of instruments, stabilization of the space platform, accurate tracking and locating of data gathered, and, finally, methods of handling and analyzing the great volumes of data generated. Certainly, in considering future operational systems of remote sensing for agricultural purposes, both air and space platforms should be studied.

The justifications for considering operational remote-sensing systems for agriculture are varied and many. Understanding of these is aided by considering the basic function of agriculture, which is the use of green plants to capture solar energy and convert elements from air, water, and soil into organic foodstuffs and fiber for men's use. It is primarily, then, a biological system, and the operations are carried out in open-air environments that vary widely and are subject to little control by the farmer.

As in any biological system, the organisms are subject to devastation by damaging agents such as disease and insect attack. Constant protective and remedial measures must be applied to maintain production. Economically, these functions for agricultural crops involve extensive business enterprises that operate not only on a local but on a national and international basis.

The world has 22 principal agricultural regions totaling nearly 4 billion acres of cropland. Crop production is a year-round operation. The planting dates of certain crops in the Northern Hemisphere coincide with the harvest periods of those crops in the areas of the Southern Hemisphere. In regions of mild climate, two or three successive crops of the same species may be grown. There is every indication that modern man will try to eliminate famine as a scourge and enhance his ability to maximize world food production by increasing the efficiency of this great productive process.

Immediate Applications

Two immediately useful applications of a worldwide view of vegetation and soil patterns were pointed out in the report of a Conference on the Use of Orbiting Spacecraft in Geographic Research held at Houston, January 28 to 30, 1965:

(1) It should be possible to improve predictions of cereal crop yields in the world's extensive semiarid farming regions by determining the state of soil moisture and incidence of disease at critical times during the growing season. Such areas will be of increasing significance as the population grows. If extended areas of crop failure in the Northern Hemisphere were foreseen, efforts to maximize production in the Southern Hemisphere might be begun in time to reduce the danger of famine.

(2) Clearing and cultivation of tropical lands is proceeding rapidly. Some of these areas will yield crops indefinitely but others will soon become sterile. Once the forest is removed from laterite soils and the land is permitted to dry out, for example, it will turn to rock impervious to water and plant roots. If such soils could be identified prior to clearing, major Earth resources could be protected and human energy saved. Potential laterites may be subject to sensing either by penetration of microwaves or by particular characteristics of the surface vegetation.

In many parts of the world there is a continuous gradation from natural vegetation that has not been affected by men to disturbed vegetation and specifically bred, commercially cultivated crops occupying entire fields of varying extent. Figure 10 is an Apollo 6 photograph of an area near Abilene, Tex., from which a great amount of detailed information can be extracted about both vegetation and soils. Uncultivated areas can be distinguished from cultivated areas (including recently plowed fields). This photo was taken in the spring, and the amount of winter wheat planted was estimated on a gross basis by measuring the dark-green rectangular fields readily visible.

California's Imperial Valley was one of the test sites chosen for the Apollo 9 experiments with multispectral imagery because it was a convenient, generally cloud-free area that offered a variety of crop and field conditions. Figure 11 was taken of this valley from an altitude of 105 n. mi. on color infrared film. Figure 12 includes three black-and-white photos of the same area taken with different films and filters.

The Salton Sea is in the upper left; Mexicali, Mexico, is in the lower center; and Yuma, Ariz., is in the lower right of these pictures. Much can be done with such photos. Beet and alfalfa fields can be distinguished. Even more than meets the eye can be learned by projecting transparencies of the black-and-white films to reconstitute colors and studying displays with filters that yield optical-density measurements for different crop types. The Apollo 9 camera system was a forerunner of one being developed for use in the first Earth Resources Technology Satellite.

When one views the characteristics of crop production in the light of the objective of removing human starvation, one is impressed by the magnitude of the task of providing agricultural information on which the nations of the world can base decisions affecting production, processing, and distribution of foodstuffs. Fortunately, we have considerable experience on which to rely. In the last 35 years the United States has evolved a rather effective crop-production control mechanism by which the volume of annual production has been regulated. The crop reporting and crop census services provide a fairly complete U.S. census each 5 years on more than 55 different crops, and each season on acres of each major crop planted and harvested, production and yield forecasts at several intervals during the growing season, and actual production estimates at harvest. All these data are extensively used by farmers, industry, and Government in planning production, regulating practices, and distributing and processing the crop products.

Statistical agricultural data in the developing food-deficit nations are frequently sketchy and unreliable. Access to crop-producing regions often is difficult because of terrain barriers and absence of all-weather roads. The possibilities of establishing aerospace multispectral remote-sensing systems are especially appealing as a giant step in the gathering of agricultural data on a world basis to help meet world food needs.

Prof. J. R. Shay of the Department of Botany and Plant Pathology, University of Oregon, was the source of much of the information in this chapter.

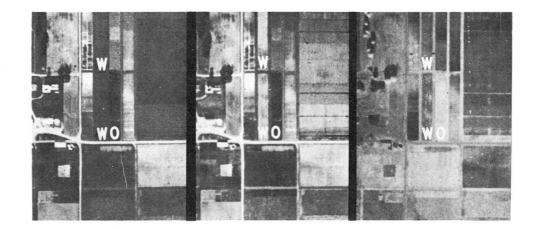

FIGURE 7

Tones of wheat (W) and oats (O) differ when recorded by an airborne multilens camera filtered to three spectral regions (0.38 to 0.44 micron, at left; 0.62 to 0.68, center; and 0.85 to 0.89, at right).

DATA COLLECTED BY PURDUE UNIVERSITY AGRONOMY FARM

FIGURE 8
Infrared photo taken from
an airplane at Weslaco,
Tex., shows crop vigor,
growth, and soil salinity:
(1) Healthy cotton, (2)
unhealthy cotton, (3) bare
soil, (4) pig weeds in wet
area, (5) pig weeds above
short sorghum, (6) dry
topsoil between rows of
sorghum, and (7) bare soil
between sorghum in moist
area.

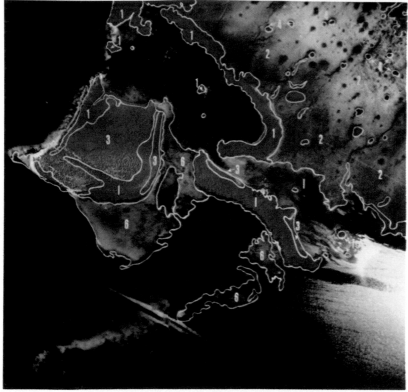

FIGURE 9
Photo taken from 5000 ft above Florida's
Everglades reveals vegetation by color:
(1) Dense mangrove jungle, (2) brackish-
water marsh with scattered dwarf mangroves, (3) mangroves occasionally flooded
by tides, (4) isolated fresh-water trees
and mangroves, (5) sawgrass, and (6)
mudflats exposed at low tides.

PREPARED IN COOPERATION WITH U.S.
GEOLOGICAL SURVEY

APOLLO 6   AS6–2—1458

FIGURE 10   The shape and color of Texas fields reveals winter wheat plantings in this Apollo 6 photo.

APOLLO 9   AS9–26a–3799a

FIGURE 11   The Imperial Valley of southern California as photographed in color infrared from Apollo 9.

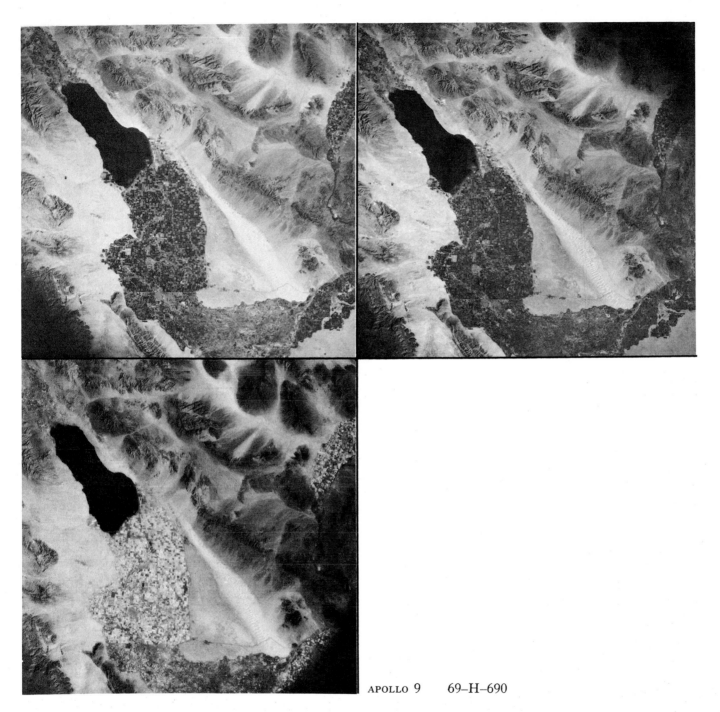

APOLLO 9   69–H–690

FIGURE 12   Three pictures, on different film with different filters, yield more data than one. The upper left photo was taken on Panatomic-X film with a green filter; the upper right picture on Panatomic-X film with a red filter, and the lower picture on black and white infrared film.

FORESTRY 4

Like the mountains and seas, the Earth's billions of acres of woodland are a storehouse of raw materials—so big that its size affects the weather. Birds, beasts, and men have long depended on forests for shelter, and wood-product industries are a major segment of the American economy. The Forest Service of the U.S. Department of Agriculture keeps a continuing inventory now of this country's timber to provide volume, growth, and drain statistics to local and national planners and legislators. Some data are as much as 9 years old when reported, however, because of the difficulties and cost of collecting information about woodlands. In many countries, much less is known than in the United States about the current condition of forest resources.

Both foresters and naturalists need surveys of large areas of terra incognita that are difficult to reach on the ground, but that can be monitored rapidly and repetitively from orbiting satellites. Such spacecraft can serve many countries virtually simultaneously. Planners especially need up-to-date information about timber and forage crops in remote regions. With the help of spacecraft, more can be learned about the type and vigor of vegetation in each physiographic unit, the identity of damaging agents or organisms, the yield of timber or forage obtainable per acre, and the total area of various physiographic units.

The test of the usefulness of space photography in forestry lies not in its beauty but in its disclosure of significant features, and how consistently interpretations of those features conform to ground truth. Remote sensors cannot provide highly detailed coverage of every acre of the Earth, but sampling systems can be developed for use with information from remote sensors.

For some Earth resource features (e.g., irrigated or mowed fields), care must be taken to acquire information on the ground at almost the same time as the space photography. For other features (e.g., reservoir levels, snowfields, timber-cutting boundaries, crop flowering, and degrees of water pollution), delays of a few hours or days in

acquiring ground truth may be tolerable; and for a few Earth resource features (e.g., certain landforms and associated mineral deposits), the acquisition of information on the ground at any time in the same geologic era may suffice.

Feasibility Findings

Both the SO–65 photography and pictures taken in conventional color with a handheld camera from Apollo 9 were studied by personnel of the Forestry Remote Sensing Laboratory of the University of California at Berkeley with the aid of reliable ground data. Results obtainable within the constraints of a report deadline are summarized in table 3, and suggest the relative feasibility of obtaining various kinds of information from such photography.

Figure 13 is an Ektachrome infrared picture taken by the Apollo 9 astronauts of the test site near Vicksburg. The Mississippi River is at the extreme right, and the area shown extends about 90 miles to the west of it in Louisiana. The long bluish blotch in the upper left quarter of the photo is a Ouachita River flood. The wide light swath running from the top to the bottom of the right half of the picture is agricultural land on a former flood plain of the Mississippi River. The dark blotches within this area are uncut patches of hardwood, and a large area of hardwood forest can be seen toward the lower-right corner of the photo. Although the seasonal state of deciduous forests affects the appearance of such areas, little difficulty is encountered in distinguishing between cultivated land and forests in space photography.

This picture was used to test multistage sampling theories, and a substantial reduction in errors was found possible. It was also an impressive demonstration of the usefulness of space photography in the study of floods.

The Ouachita River flood shown covered about 165 square miles and contained about a million acre-feet of

(*Continued on page 24*)

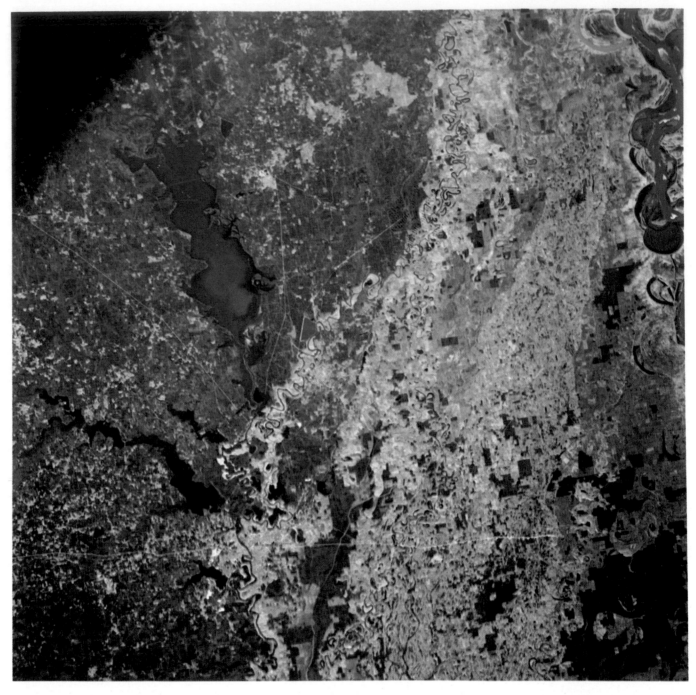

APOLLO 9   AS9–26a–3740a

FIGURE 13   An Apollo 9 infrared photo of agricultural and forest land in Louisiana near the Mississippi.

TABLE 3   FEASIBILITY OF DETECTING EARTH RESOURCE
FEATURES ON APOLLO 9 PHOTOGRAPHY

Type of Earth resource feature	Photographic film-filter combination				
	Black-and-white photos			Color photos	
	Pan-58 (green)	Pan-25A (red)	Infrared-89B (infrared)	Ektachrome (normal color)	Infrared Ektachrome (false color)
Vegetation Resources:					
Vegetated or not	−	+	+	+	++
Natural or cultivated vegetation	+	+	+	+	++
Trees, shrubs, or herbaceous vegetation	+	+	+	+	++
Hardwoods or conifers	−	−	−	−	+
Individual tree species	−	−	−	−	−−
Chaparral, desert shrub, or other shrub type	−	−	−	+	+
Individual shrub species	−−	−−	−−	−−	−−
Annual or perennial herbaceous type	−−	−−	−	−	−
Individual herbaceous species	−−	−−	−−	−−	−−
Orchards	−	−	−	+	+
Continuous cover crops	−	+	+	++	++
Individual crop types	−−	−−	−−	−	−
Vegetation density	−	+	+	+	++
Vegetation vigor	−	−	+	−	+

++ =Signifies that the resource feature is *consistently identifiable* by most photointerpreters on space photographs flown to the specifications indicated; only rarely is a mistake made.

+ =Signifies that the resource feature is *usually identifiable* on the space photographs; however, to avoid numerous mistakes, care must be taken that the photointerpretation is done by personnel having a strong background of training and experience in the resource discipline involved (e.g., forestry, agriculture, range management).

− =Signifies that the resource feature is *usually unidentifiable* on space photography flown to the specifications indicated; however, with moderate improvement either in image quality or photointerpretation skill, most "−" ratings could be converted to "+".

− − =Signifies that, important though the resource feature may be, it is *consistently unidentifiable* on space photography flown to the specifications indicated.

water. It resulted mainly from a rain on January 30, 1969, that ranged from less than an inch at some measurement stations to more than 8 in. at others and averaged about 4 in. over the drainage basin. Another rain on February 22 added about an inch to sustain the flood. Its duration was increased, too, by a natural levee of the Bayou Bartholomew that constricts the outflow. The flood peak, February 17 to 19, was 74.42 ft above mean sea level, and still 72.69 ft on March 8 when this photo was taken. Although such floods are not unusual, few have been delineated this way in a single photograph.

Insect and Fire Detection

The colors in infrared photos are not those that the eye sees, but represent variations in the reflectance of light.

Figure 14 is an aerial photo that shows how such photography can be used to detect and assess damage done to silver fir trees by balsam woolly aphids. This picture was taken southeast of Portland, Ore., in the course of experiments by the U.S. Forest Service with infrared imaging. Damaged trees often show up clearly in infrared pictures before the human eye can distinguish them. This is because the infrared rays penetrate the leaves, and the internal cells of the leaves on unhealthy trees cease to reflect such waves sooner than the surface cells stop reflecting the wavelengths utilized by the eye.

Studies conducted by NASA have shown that signatures such as those in figure 14 that are indicative of tree health and the extent of damaged areas can be obtained

(*Continued on page 28*)

FIGURE 14   Damaged trees are blue green and healthy trees are red or pink in this aerial Ektachrome infrared photo.

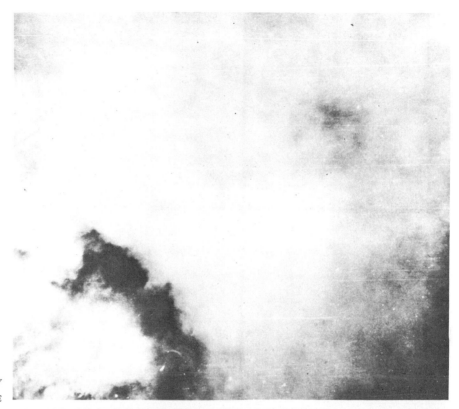

Figure 15(*a*)

A conventional aerial photo
(*a*) and an infrared photo (*b*)
of an uncontrolled fire on
September 19, 1964.

COURTESY OF U.S. FORESTRY
SERVICE

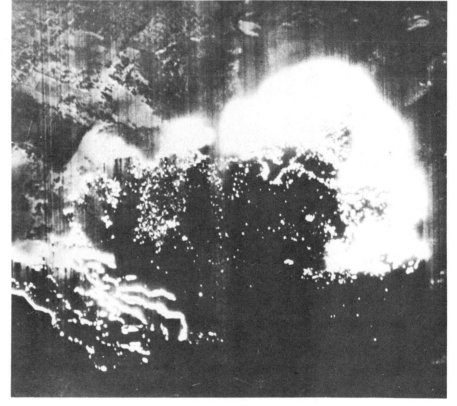

Figure 15(*b*)

GEMINI 7   S65–64053

FIGURE 16   An infrared photo of the Gulf coast showing two plumes of smoke from forest fires December 7, 1965.

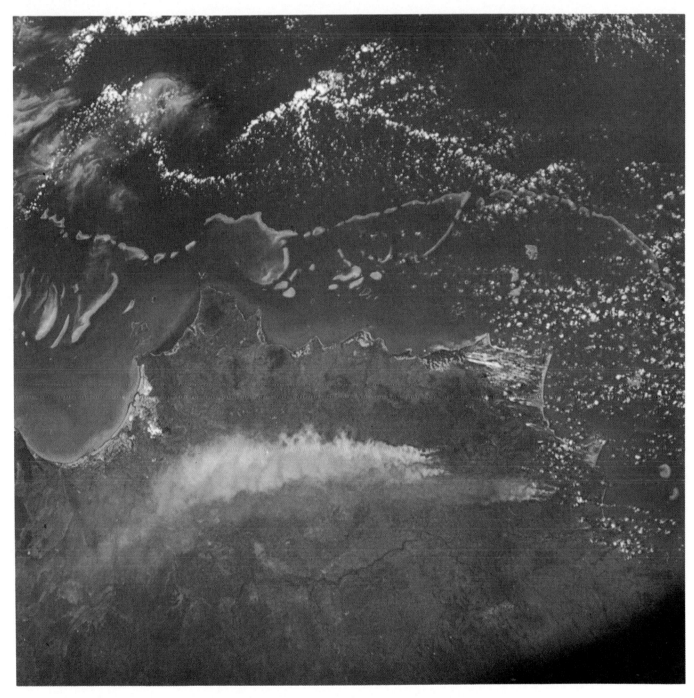

APOLLO 7   AS7–8–1902

FIGURE 17   An Apollo 7 picture of forest fires in northern Australia, taken at an altitude of 150 miles.

from orbital altitudes with apparatus well within the reach of existing technology. Space vehicles with appropriate sensing equipment consequently offer men a new means of surveying large areas rapidly and frequently to estimate the extent of insect damage to forests.

Infrared sensory imagery also has been shown to be useful in the detection of forest fires. In some parts of the world, fires seem to have affected the vegetation as much as the climate and soil. The flatwoods of Florida, for example, have been subjected to repeated burnings for centuries, but the consequences are not clearly understood. Students of this area now believe that if fires were completely eliminated, a climax forest of evergreen and deciduous hardwoods would become dominant in less than 20 years.

The localization, extent, frequency, and temporal predictability of fires throughout the world is far from adequately known. Fairly simple scanning systems probably could be developed to sense fires from spacecraft surveying the whole Earth. For at least a few weeks after a major burn, the ground should give a quite characteristic signature, so that the extent of the loss could be measured. With such information available on a world scale, much more might soon be learned about the relation that fires have had to the distribution of forest, brush, grasslands, and savannas.

Figure 15(a) is an aerial photo of a Nuns Canyon fire, in the Sonoma District, California, taken in the conventional way for the U.S. Forestry Service; and figure 15(b) is an infrared picture of the same fire. In the latter, the location of the flames can be pinpointed because the infrared sensor "sees" through the smoke. Such imagery also can indicate the size of a burned area while smoke still lingers over it.

Fires were evident in several of the Gemini photos; figure 16 is one taken while the spacecraft was drifting across the Gulf of Mexico. The extent of the coastal land is indicated by a narrow band of gray, and the vegetation on the swampy tidal flats is reddish in this picture. The hook-shaped sandbar in the foreground encloses St. Joseph Bay, and the long blue plume extending toward the bottom of the picture is smoke from a forest fire. Another such plume is visible to the right. Both plumes were from forest areas southwest of Tallahassee, Fla.

Figure 17 is a more recent and dramatic example of space photography. It shows the Great Barrier Reef, Cape Melville, Cape Flattery, and Queensland, Australia, as they appeared to the Apollo 7 astronauts on their 115th revolution of the Earth. Although taken from an altitude of 150 n. mi., this picture clearly shows the plumes from forest fires.

Information for this chapter was drawn largely from papers by R. N. Colwell, Director of the Forestry Remote Sensing Laboratory, University of California, Berkeley; W. T. Mealor, Jr., and Merle C. Prunty, University of Georgia; and Philip G. Langley, Robert C. Aldrich, and Robert C. Heller of the U.S. Forest Service.

GEOLOGY 5

Twentieth-century geologists urgently need more knowledge on both a regional and global basis about the extent and location of mineral and petroleum deposits. Men have used more of these "nonrenewable" resources in the last three decades than in all of the previous years since the dawn of civilization, and proven reserves of several such resources are liable to be exhausted within the next 20 years.

To husband the remaining accumulations of useful materials properly, we need both better estimates of their magnitude and better means of discovering them. Global observations made year after year from spacecraft could enhance the geologists' understanding of the dynamics of the Earth, and at the same time help the prospectors now industriously examining both its continents and its sea floors. A more careful inventory is necessary to formulate wise policies governing the use of these natural resources.

Coastal Desert Studies

The next four color photographs are Gemini 5 pictures taken only a minute apart high over South-West Africa. They cover a zone more than 100 miles wide and nearly 400 miles long, extending roughly from longitude 14° E and 21.5° S to 20° E and 25° S. Figures 18 and 19 overlap considerably and figures 20 and 21 overlap slightly. The scale varies because of tip and tilt within each photo and between photos; the maps alongside each picture show geologic features identifiable by students.

The first two photos show an economically important area on the Atlantic coast, where the Benguela current has shaped the sand into a series of huge hooks. Walvis Bay, the chief port for this part of Africa, is inside the uppermost sandhook in figure 18, protected from the Atlantic by 5-mile-long Pelican Point. A strip of the coast extending south out of this picture is a restricted diamond mining area. Figures 20 and 21 are views of the terrain near Windhoek in Damaraland.

The sand dunes in the lower half of figure 18 are bounded by the Kuiseb River, but even major rivers in this part of the world are intermittent streams. Vegetation is sparse and absent in many parts of this region, and when found is usually concentrated along streams and in the higher areas encompassed by the photos. It is easily confused in the pictures with dark rocks and shadows.

The most obvious features visible here from the spacecraft are the large drifting sand dunes that completely cover the bedrock, and broad pediments or bedrock areas with a very thin wash of Recent to Quaternary alluvium. Inselbergs and small rock outcrops in the pediments are numerous. Large ridges and hilly areas are mostly bare rock onto which the wind has blown sand and alluvium. These areas reflect striking gross structural features such as joints, foliation, bedding, faults, and folds. According to the UNESCO geologic map of Africa (1963) and Du Toit's *The Geology of Africa* (1955), large areas of bedrock are metamorphosed sedimentary complexes of Precambrian age and variously aged igneous extrusives and intrusives. In the complexes, schist and some beds that probably are marble and quartzite are indicated on the maps.

No effort was made in the maps presented here to correlate precisely all published geologic reports with the photos. The interpretations here were the work of first-year graduate students in geology under the supervision of Dr. Robert F. Black at the University of Wisconsin. The objective was to point out the larger and more obvious features identifiable from the photos, rather than to read into them details that could not be seen, even though much more information might have been gleaned with the help of governmental surveys and mining company maps.

Figure 22 shows an area lying on the Iran-Iraq border. The Tigris River traverses the photograph at the upper left. The camera lens was of 80-mm focal length, and the orbital altitude of Gemini 5 was roughly 150

(*Continued on page 38*)

N
APPROXIMATE

FIGURE 18   A Gemini 5 photo of the Atlantic coast of Africa north and south of the port of Walvis Bay.

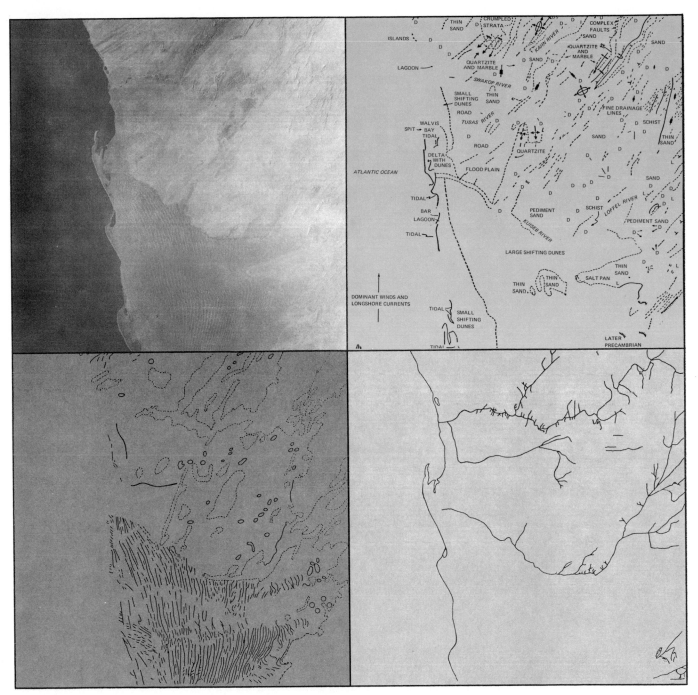

FIGURE 18 (Continued)   (a) Major land forms. (b) Lithologic boundaries, bedding, and schistosity. (c) Sand rock boundaries, dune crests and roads. (d) Intermittent streams.

a	b
c	d

Intermittent streams	Faults	L — Later Precambrian rocks. Mostly metamorphosed sandstones, schist, etc.
Sand-rock boundaries	High angle joints	
Dune crest	Anticline	D — Damara system. Early Precambrian, schists, marbles, quartzites
Lithologic boundaries	Syncline	
Roads	Dome	I — Intrusives of uncertain age. Granitic rocks.
Bedding and schistosity	Strike and dip of bedding	Sand, thin sand, pediment sand, dunes, etc., Pleistocene and/or Recent
Prominent escarpment		

GEMINI   S65–45579

FIGURE 19   Another view of the coast of South-West Africa that overlaps the one reproduced in figure 18.

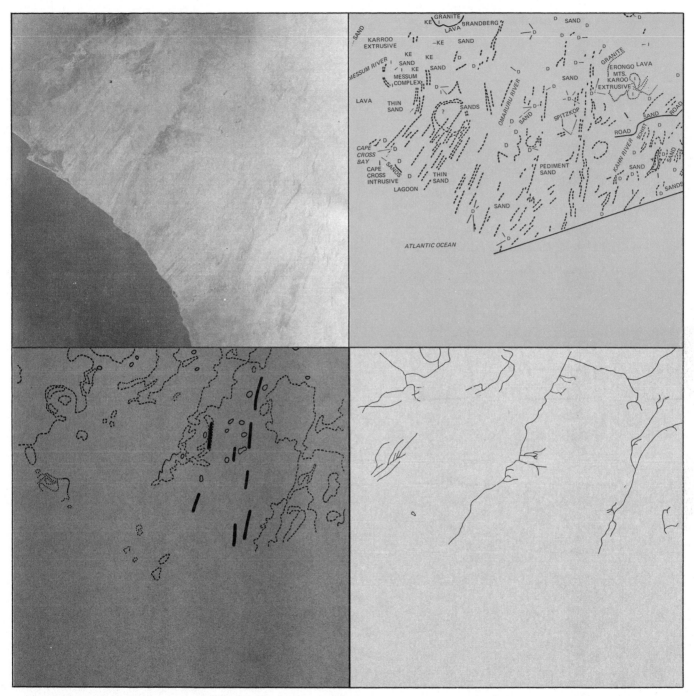

FIGURE 19 (Continued)   (a) Desert geology. (b) Lithologic boundaries, bedding, and schistosity. (c) Rock sand boundaries and trend of possible dikes or dike swarms. (d) Intermittent streams.

a	b
c	d

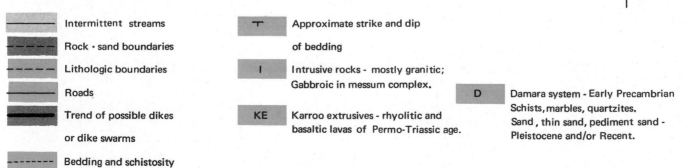

Intermittent streams

Rock · sand boundaries

Lithologic boundaries

Roads

Trend of possible dikes
or dike swarms

Bedding and schistosity

Approximate strike and dip
of bedding

Intrusive rocks - mostly granitic;
Gabbroic in messum complex.

KE   Karroo extrusives - rhyolitic and
basaltic lavas of Permo-Triassic age.

D   Damara system - Early Precambrian
Schists, marbles, quartzites.
Sand, thin sand, pediment sand -
Pleistocene and/or Recent.

FIGURE 20   Somewhat heavier vegetation was recorded as Gemini 5 moved over the mainland of South-West Africa.

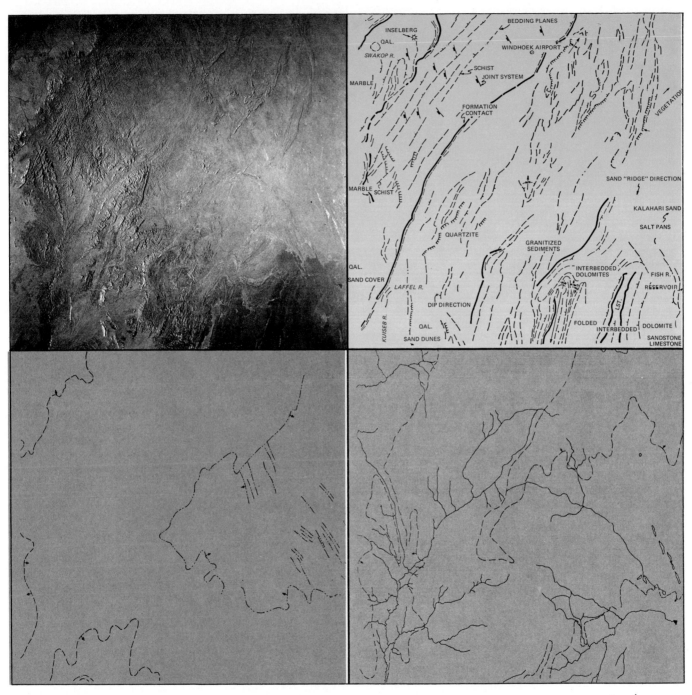

FIGURE 20 (Continued)   (a) Major land forms. (b) Dip and strike and other features. (c) Sand dunes and ridges. (d) Stream channels and vegetation.

a	b
c	d

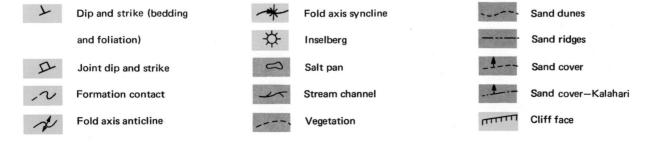

GEMINI 5   S65–45581

FIGURE 21   Another picture, taken immediately after figure 20, of the Windhoek area of South-West Africa.

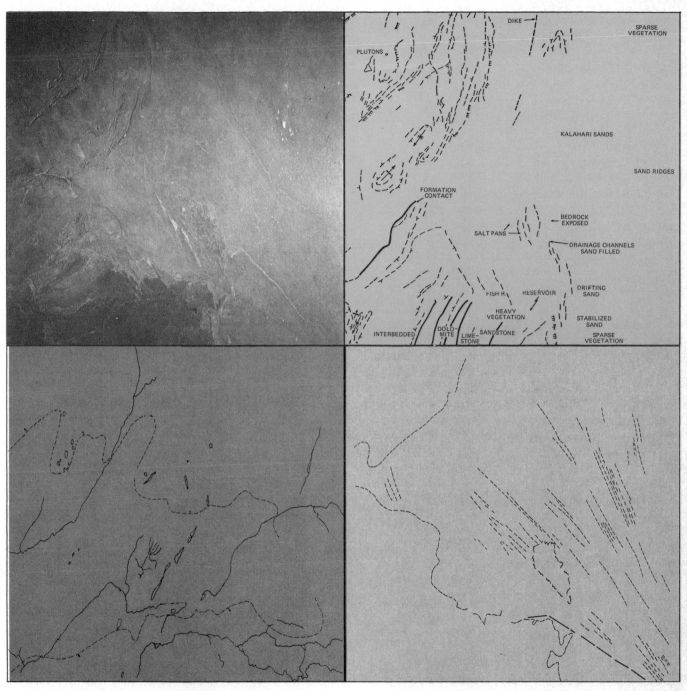

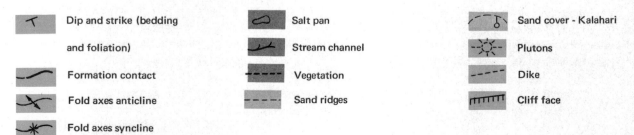

FIGURE 21 (Continued)   (a) Desert geology. (b) Formation contacts, anticlines, and synclines. (c) Sand ridges. (d) Stream channels and vegetation.

a	b
c	d

miles; the film scale works out to be about 1 : 3 000 000.

The Zagros Mountains, which consist of strongly folded sedimentary rocks, extend across the lower right-hand portion of this photograph. These deformed rock layers can be seen in long folds alined generally parallel to one another and broken by occasional faults. Toward the upper left, the folds diminish in amplitude and are farther apart as they disappear under the alluvium of the Mesopotamian plain.

Interpretation of the geologic structure is here a fairly straightforward task. The direction in which a rock layer dips (the direction in which its surface is inclined) can be seen most readily on stereoscopic pairs of photographs, and with properly made stereoscopic pairs, the angle of inclination can be measured. On a single photograph, such as figure 22, an interpreter relies on less direct clues than the immediately visible spatial relationships seen in a stereo view. These are the presence of *cuestas* and *flatirons,* the relations between shadows and highlights, and the characteristics that make outcrop bands of different strata distinguishable from one another: differences in photographic tone, differences in texture, and differences in topographic expression (some rocks tend to form ridges; others, valleys). When an interpreter has acquired a feeling for the relationship between the surface view and the three-dimensional structure of a mass of folded rock layers, he is able to see a coherent pattern in the map view presented in an aerial photograph, and to reconstruct, within limits, the three-dimensional structure from that view.

Above the lake in figure 22 there is a pattern of intersecting rectangular lines. Such a pattern can only be artificial, and its position relative to the river suggests that it is a system of irrigation canals. But the lines in the photograph seem to be too wide to be produced by canals, and the explanation of this is that each canal is flanked by a moist area and increased growth of vegetation.

Structural Geology of Arabia

Figure 23 is a Gemini 4 photograph of southwest Saudi Arabia that portrays the ruggedness of arid landforms. This area appears to be geologically complex and to contain a wide variety of physical features. Although difficult to locate precisely, the area shown is at approximately 45° E and 16° N.

Most of the upper half of the photograph is occupied by a range of rugged mountains composed of igneous rocks. Toward the base is an expanse of sedimentary rocks that dip very gently toward the upper right of the photo-

graph. The distinction between igneous and sedimentary rocks is made by noting the presence of stratification, or layering, in sedimentary rocks. These two units appear to be separated by a major fault.

In the upper-right corner is an area covered by dune sands. The elongated forms are seif dunes, alined parallel to the prevailing wind direction. Smaller dune forms visible are either transverse or barchan dunes, which are oriented with their long dimensions perpendicular to the prevailing wind. Projecting through the sand are inselbergs, isolated erosional remnants of bedrock.

A river flows toward the top of the photograph at the right. Its wide, braided channel indicates that it is clogged with sediment, and carries water in periodic torrential floods, having relatively small flow most of the time. To the left of the river, a series of alluvial fans have grown together to form a continuous slope away from the mountain front. On its surface, a dichotomic pattern of drainage is visible—the primary streams branching downstream as they leave the mountain front.

The most striking feature of this photograph is the well-developed pattern of fracture lines visible in the igneous rock. Such fracture systems are by no means unusual; they exist everywhere on Earth, and are visible in all kinds of materials, although igneous rocks generally show more numerous fractures than sedimentary rocks or soils. The expression of fractures is also generally more subtle in sedimentary rocks and in soils. The fractures appear at a casual glance to be randomly oriented; but statistical analyses of fracture patterns in many areas have shown that the whole fracture system is generally composed of four sets, each with a dominant mean orientation. It is widely believed that the orientation of these fracture sets reflects the stress system in the Earth's crust.

Some economic use has been made of this theory, notably in exploration for oil and gas. Because inhomogeneities in the Earth's crust, such as domal structures that might be traps for oil, cause disturbances in the stress system, they produce local changes in the fracture pattern. These local changes, or anomalies, can be found by statistical analysis of fractures or by a qualitative kind of interpretation. Experience has shown that features such as domal structures are often overlain on the Earth's surface by anomalous patterns of fracture lines that appear as branching or diverging lines. Good examples of such patterns can be seen in figure 23. In the area of sedimentary rocks, a probable subsurface domal structure is inferred, not from the fracture pattern, but from the apparent

(*Continued on page 42*)

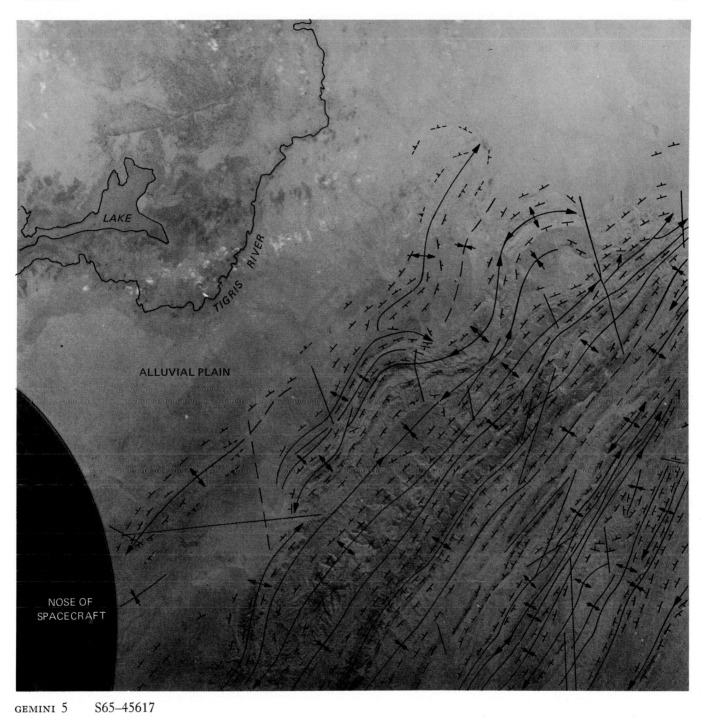

LAKE

TIGRIS RIVER

ALLUVIAL PLAIN

NOSE OF
SPACECRAFT

GEMINI 5   S65–45617

⟨ Dip and strike of strata ·   ⟶ Plunge of fold axis

Anticlinal fold axis   ⸻ Fault

Synclinal fold axis

FIGURE 22   An area of about 115 square miles including the Tigris River flood plain and the Zagros Mountains.

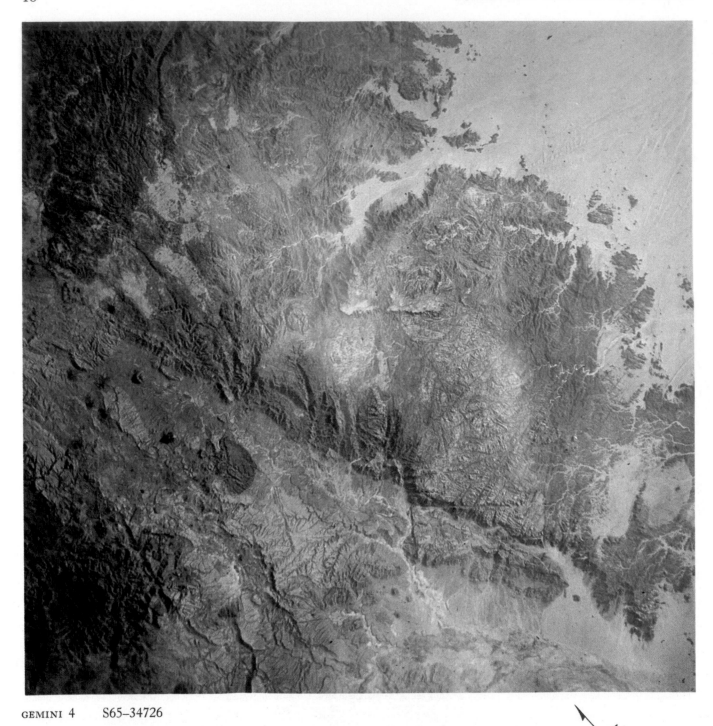

GEMINI 4   S65–34726

FIGURE 23   The structural geology of Saudi Arabia and Yemen is evident in this Gemini 4 photograph.

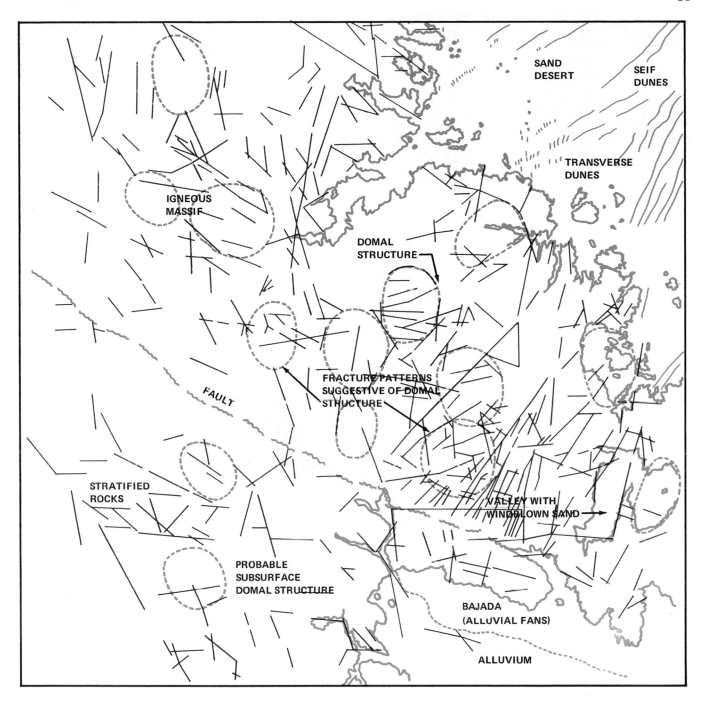

FIGURE 23 (Continued)   Details of the photo on the facing page of interest to geologists.

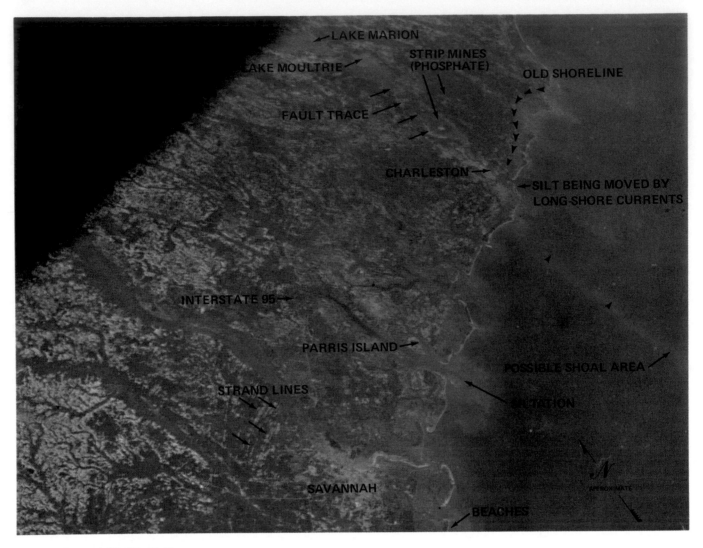

APOLLO 9   AS9–20–3148

FIGURE 24   An Apollo 9 photo of the shoreland between Charleston, S.C., and Savannah, Ga.

change in dip of the bedding and the annular pattern formed by the surface drainage.

Geologic processes continue whether men notice or ignore them, but leave features that sometimes become more noticeable when viewed from high altitudes. Figure 24 is a photo taken of the Atlantic coast of the United States by the Apollo 9 astronauts. The linear feature indicated west of Charleston, S.C., in this picture may be the unmapped trace of a fault that may have caused a major earthquake in 1886. In the left center, strand lines can be seen that

mark the raised beaches of older shorelines. Off the shore now, one can see river sediments being deposited as much as 3 miles from effluents, and possible offshore shoals appear as light bands up to 10 miles from the mainland between Charleston and Savannah, Ga.

Repetitive photography from spacecraft can help geologists assess coastal changes, whether men or natural phenomena are responsible for them. Space surveys may direct attention, in time to avert serious difficulties, to many developments that should be studied in detail.

Evaluations of photography in this chapter were obtained from the work of James F. Miller, Albert F. Allong, and Robert E. Black of the University of Wisconsin; A. G. Franklin of Northwestern University; and William D. Carter, William R. Hemphill, and Allan N. Kover of the U.S. Geological Survey.

HYDROLOGY 6

Hydrologists emphasize that water already has become the most limiting and valuable resource in some parts of the world. Rapidly receding water tables suggest that in many areas inadequate fresh-water supplies may soon limit food production and even human occupancy. To manage the water resources of the Earth more intelligently, we need more information about the surface and subsurface flows of water, the locations of aquifers, and the suitability of various sites for constructing dams and impounding water. Numerous pictures taken by both the Gemini and the Apollo astronauts have indicated how photography from spacecraft could be helpful to hydrologists.

Increasing the moisture of soil decreases its reflectivity, which makes moist soils appear dark. Photographs consequently are quite sensitive indicators of relative soil moisture, even where vegetation has not been affected. On the far side of the Tigris River shown in figure 22 (in the preceding chapter) is one end of a large lake that, judging from the pattern of dark tones around it, varies in size and is now at a low stage. Between the lake and river are distributaries—subsidiary streams that carry water *away* from the main stream and which branch downstream. Such streams deposit large quantities of fine-grained sediment. The point of land projecting into the head of the lake is a delta composed of these sediments. In addition to damp ground around variable lakes, the soil moistened by a passing thunderstorm can be mapped from space photography. This is illustrated by the dark finger extending from the lower left-hand corner of figure 25 (an oblique photograph of the Midland, Tex., area) to the upper central portion of the photograph.

Drainage Lines

In addition to the thunderstorm pattern, figure 25 shows the drainage pattern of the region. This area has few prominent geological features; the surface is covered with alluvial and windblown deposits, and the bedrock strata are nearly horizontal and but little folded. Nevertheless, there are important deposits of oil and gas in this region. These are often in anticlinal or domal structures that have very little surface expression. Some such deposits have been found by interpretations of anomalous patterns of drainage or fractures shown on aerial photographs. Several anomalies that might be associated with domal structures are indicated in the photograph here.

Subsurface structures, either domes or basins, are often expressed at the ground surface by slight topographic highs or depressions even in places where there is a considerable thickness of soil or unconsolidated sediment. Streams may be deflected to flow around topographic highs, or a high may form a pattern of flow away from its center in all directions—a "radial drainage." In some cases, the elevation is insufficient to deflect the stream but may change the gradient of the stream, thereby affecting the complex interrelationship of stream gradient, meander habit, channel width, channel depth, and channel shape. For this reason, any localized change in the channel character of a stream that cannot be explained by surface effects may indicate a subsurface anticline or dome.

Anomalous fracture patterns, called linear anomalies, often take the form of divergent fracture traces or changes in the direction of fracture traces. One such anomaly is indicated on figure 25. Also prominent in space photographs are several cases of control of the courses of stream channels by fractures.

Three basic considerations in determining the drainage lines within an area covered by the satellite photograph are tonal contrast, pattern, and intuitive feel for the environment. It is not possible to say which is the most important of these three considerations, for it is the subjective interplay that matters. In any given area, however, one or two considerations probably become dominant.

The use of tonal contrast to trace the drainage lines depends upon the texture of the terrain and, to a lesser de-

(*Continued on page 48*)

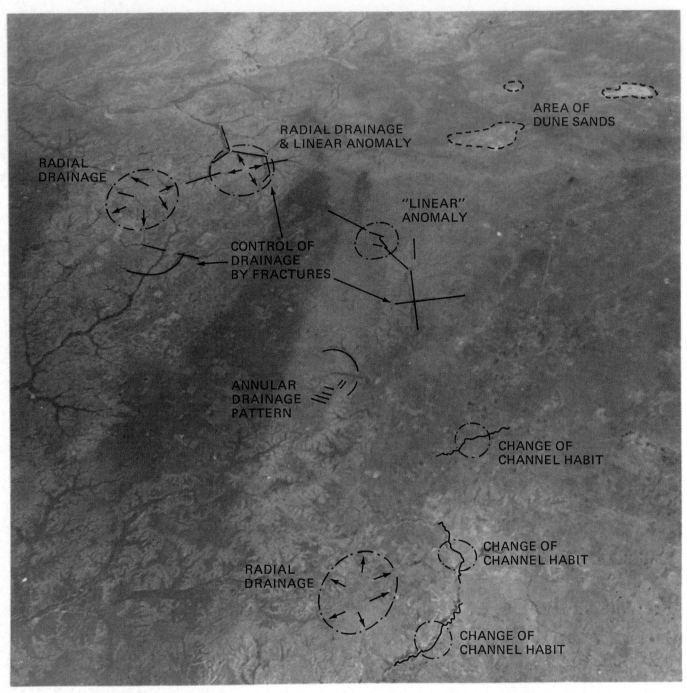

GEMINI 4   S65–34704

FIGURE 25   Western Texas near Midland and Odessa, with the Concho River drainage system at the lower left.

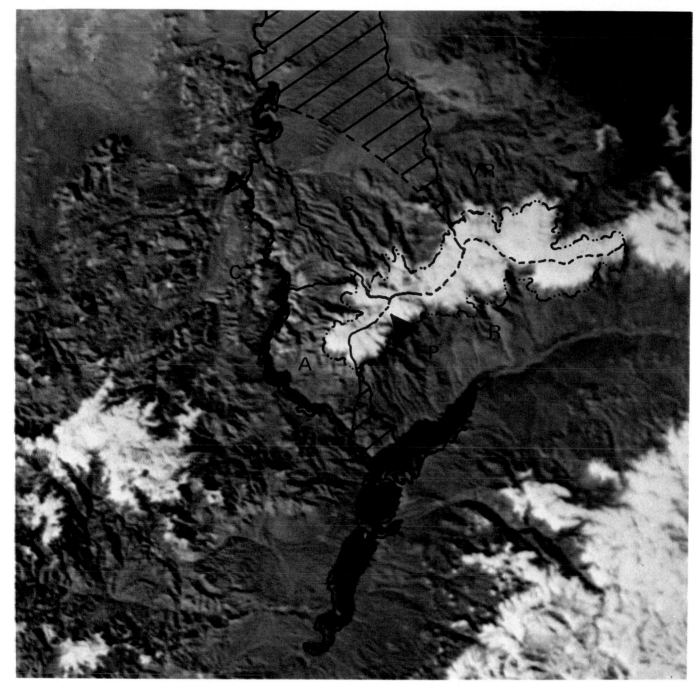

AS9–26a–3802a

– – – – – –   Snow

FIGURE 26   An Apollo 9 photo of snow destined for Apache Lake (A), Canyon Lake (C), Four Peaks (FP), Roosevelt Lake (R), Saguaro Lake (S), and Verde River (VR) as seen on Arizona's Mazatzal Mountains.

GEMINI 4   S65–34673

FIGURE 27   The mouth of the Colorado River and islands at the northern end of the Gulf of California.

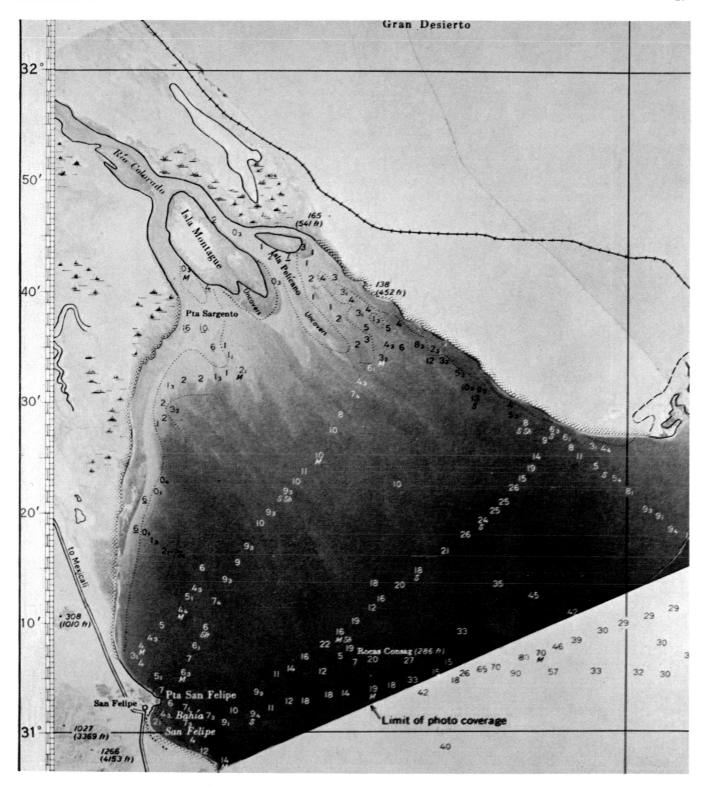

FIGURE 28   Experimental chartlet of the Gulf of California's Colorado River delta derived from H.O. Chart 620.

gree, upon the angle at which a satellite photograph is taken with respect to the surface of the Earth and incident sunlight. Rough terrain, probably because of its relief, shadows, and vegetation, often appears in a photograph in dark hues, and within these areas the drainage lines commonly have a light color. In figure 37 (chap. 8) the irrigated croplands along the Rio Grande River contrast with the light aspect of the river itself. Presumably, the rather light tone to the drainage lines in these circumstances results from the alluvial material in the stream channels, and the predominance of siliceous materials in the alluvium. This assumption seems reasonable in the area analyzed, for sedimentary formations are evident, and presumably these sediments have a normal amount of siliceous material in them. On the other hand, relatively smooth, featureless areas tend to be rather light colored, and by contrast the drainage lines may be seen because waterways are somewhat incised into the surface, thus creating relief, shade, and darker tones; or possibly the moisture associated with the waterways and alluvium is manifest in darker tones. Incident sunlight in some cases appears to flood incised drainage channels, and consequently the distinctness of the drainage line is at least partially lost.

A second means of identifying drainage lines stems from the pattern produced on the landscape, and this depends mainly upon the lithology and attitude of underlying geologic formations. In the central portion of the photograph (fig. 37), and within the irrigated cropland area of the Rio Grande Valley, a number of sinuous lines are visible. The sinuosity of the lines and their location with respect to the slope and lay of the land give rather clear evidence that they are natural rather than manmade landscape features, and, therefore, must be drainage lines. An intuitive feel for environments enters into all determinations of drainage lines.

In many areas the bulk of the annual runoff occurs in the spring and summer when the winter's snowpack from high mountains reaches a drainage basin. It is often desirable to estimate this seasonal runoff to plan flood-control measures, irrigation, and other activities. To test the feasibility of using space photography to assign each part of a snowpack to its receiving reservoir, the Four Peaks area in the Mazatzal Mountains east of Phoenix in central Arizona, was selected.

Figure 26 is a portion of an Apollo 9 photo on which lines have been drawn indicating the destination of the snow in the field shown. Areas where no melt water will flow are hatched. A more reliable delineation probably could be made if stereo coverage were available, and this possibility is currently being studied.

Water Depths

Zonal patterns in shallow-water bodies can often be used to infer the depth of the water. How this may be done is illustrated by color photographs exposed during the Gemini 4 flight in June 1965 that were selected for evaluation by the U.S. Naval Oceanographic Office. The purpose of this evaluation was to determine the possible utilization of similar photography derived from other satellites in the future. Manned space vehicles offer great versatility for obtaining high-quality photography for hydrographic and oceanographic analyses. Near-vertical photographic coverage in color, black and white, or infrared over extensive land and sea areas is possible from a single space vehicle (fig. 27).

An uncontrolled mosaic of two color prints was prepared for the evaluation. A film positive of part of H.O. Chart 620 was scaled to fit the shoreline from the Colorado River Delta area to Point San Felipe. An overall fit of the chart shoreline to the mosaic was not feasible. The color photos could not be printed as rectified prints without going through several optical steps, each of which would deteriorate the tonal quality of the photos. The Mercator projection of H.O. Chart 620 also contained shape distortions that made it impossible to fit the photos accurately to the chart.

The coastline was traced from the photo mosaic and incorporated with other chart features from H.O. Chart 620. This graphic was then overprinted on the mosaic to form an experimental chartlet using a new method of continuous tone printing. The mosaic without the overprinted chart data was also reproduced. The result is shown in figure 28. The soundings have not been adjusted to the shoreline on the chartlet; therefore, the chartlet should not be used for navigation. Soundings in the delta area were deleted on the mosaic to avoid cluttering the detail.

The change in the photographic color of the water near the river mouth ranging from brown or gray in the shallow waters to dark blue in deeper water gives an apparently clear picture of the deposition pattern in the delta area and beyond. Because the tide stage at the time of photographic exposure was only 0.6 ft above the tidal datum of mean low water, it can be assumed that the discoloration was caused by the bottom sedimentation.

Inspection of the bottom portrayed on the stereoscopic black-and-white photo pairs confirms that the pattern of the underwater mud or sand ridges was much like that of the striated color pattern on the satellite photos. One of these black-and-white photographs covers an area approxi-

(*Continued on page 50*)

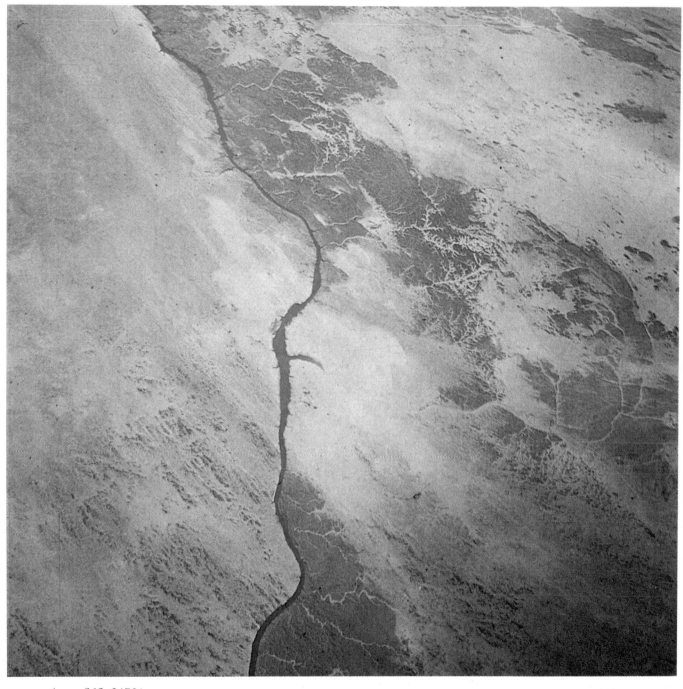

GEMINI 4   S65–34781

FIGURE 29   A satellite photo of the Nile Valley area where the Aswan Dam will create a huge new reservoir.

mately 0.9 in. square on the mosaic. To obtain stereoscopic coverage of the chart-mosaic area with photography at the same scale (1: 64 000) would require 105 photographs. The smaller scale color photography enables the viewer to get an overall view of the bottom characteristics rather than having to rely on numerous photographs in shades of gray.

The *Sailing Directions* report that, from San Felipe to the Colorado River, mud flats and shoals extend 1½ to 6 miles offshore. Also, there is evidence that much deposition has taken place in a southward direction, as shown by the striated color bands extending from the river channel. There is much less deposition, however, adjacent to the eastern shoreline. This phenomenon appears to confirm the findings in the study of delta formation in the Mississippi River Delta area. Apparently, coriolis force acting on the river discharge causes the major portion of the sediments to be carried to the west in the Northern Hemisphere. The winds at the mouth of the river are mostly from the north. Another important factor in the deposition pattern is the speed of tidal currents, which reaches 5 or 6 knots at the river mouth.

The chartlet shows a potential application for small-scale color photography. Relatively inaccessible areas could be photographed from a space vehicle using cameras designed to obtain photography suitable for small-scale stereoscopic compilation or for rapid printing of small-scale prints or photo mosaics in lieu of conventional methods.

The pattern of detail on the printed color mosaic would be difficult to portray equally well on a conventionally compiled chart. Much ground detail is not recorded, however, on the color photographs at this scale (approxi-

mately 1: 675 000). This is partly because of the enlargement process; more detail could be expected to show on the original film. Consag Rock (Rocas Consaga) shown on H.O. Chart 620 is guano covered, 286 ft high, but of small extent. It could not be seen on the color photos. Another factor requiring consideration is the difficulty of fitting a small-scale photograph containing distortions resulting from Earth curvature and nonverticality to a chart projection suitable for navigation.

From the information obtained from the Gemini color photos, it is clear that this type of photography could be used for obtaining a synoptic picture over a large area for ice reconnaissance, for oceanographic and hydrographic survey planning, for obtaining information about inaccessible areas, for interpretation of geologic structures, for supplementing other data in ocean current studies, and as an aid in updating small-scale charts.

Figure 29 is a Gemini 4 photo of the Nile Valley that shows where Lake Nasser's shoreline is expected to be when the Aswan High Dam is completed. A whole new pattern may be etched on the Earth's surface here by the development of new communities, transfer of agricultural systems, and construction of transportation and communication networks. Satellite photography before, during, and after these changes could provide a perspective and information difficult to attain from field investigations. It would offer insight into the effects of the impounded water on the landscape and the consequences of resettlement of thousands of people. Records could be kept of changes in the atmospheric humidity, in environmental temperature, and in the vegetation brought about by any manmade lake such as the one that is changing the Nile Valley now.

A. G. Franklin of Northwestern University and Donald D. MacPhail, Albert W. Smith, and Donald E. Vermeer of the University of Colorado provided interpretations of the photos in this chapter.

OCEANOGRAPHY 7

"Like those in the last century who tilled a plot of land to exhaustion and then moved on to another," President Nixon wrote in a message to Congress February 11, 1970, "we in this century have too casually and too long abused our natural environment. The time has come when we can wait no longer to repair the damage already done and to establish new criteria to guide us in the future. . . .

"While adopting laws prohibiting injury to persons or property, we have freely allowed injury to our surroundings. Conditioned by an expanding frontier, we came only lately to a recognition of how precious and how vulnerable our resources of land, water, and air really are."

Oceanographers remind us that the greatest and least-tapped natural resource of the Earth is the ocean. It is important not only as a rich source of minerals and food but also because its effect on climate can govern the habitability of much of the land surface of the world, and because oceanographic features determine the safety with which men can travel on the surface or near the surface of three-fourths of the globe. Better oceanographic inventories of many kinds are needed. The data now available are too meager regarding, for example, sea states, shoals, tsunamis, potassium, plankton, sardines, temperature, and turbidity.

Currents and Sandbars

The face of the ocean as well as the face of the land "looks to the sky," and much can be learned about shorelines, banks, lagoons, bays, oil slicks, and other such aspects of the Earth by obtaining single photographs that encompass vast areas. Six views from space of coastal regions are presented and discussed in this chapter.

Figure 30, a Gemini photo of Laguna de Terminos, Campeche, Yucatan, shows more than 10 000 square miles of the Earth's surface. Such coverage makes possible logical deductions regarding interrelated coastal processes.

Some of the prominent features here are longshore and offshore currents and a sandbar development. An easterly longshore current is made visible by the sediments discharged into the Gulf of Mexico's clear water by a river immediately to the left of the photo margin. The sediments are light-colored marls, silts, and sands. To the right of the laguna, the sandbar development is clearly visible. These bars, within a 3-fathom-depth interval, have a distinct pattern that also indicates the direction of the current. The clarity of the gulf water is quite evident here.

Other notable processes indicated by the photo are tidal fluctuations that have scored the inlets to the laguna, fresh-water discharge to the east, structural remnants of high-water action along the coast both left and right of the laguna, and a clearly discernible cloud-cover pattern. From pictures such as this, many conclusions can be drawn without recourse to other sources of information.

Figure 31 depicts the extreme southern part of Florida including the string of limestone islands forming the Florida Keys. The grand scope of the portrayal is what distinguishes satellite photographs. This is true in rugged country where the variability of topography would mask areal groupings as well as in the flat landscape of southern Florida. This photo allows the landform trends to be traced throughout southern Florida, and especially highlights the areal associations that are so intricately a part of this low-relief topography.

As this area is largely dominated by a shallow-water environment, maps, charts, and photos should give some indication of the submarine topography as well as the subaerial features. The satellite photos (especially in color) are unequaled in the depiction of subaqueous configuration.

Both the overall trends of the bottom topography and specific features, such as the contrast between vegetated and nonvegetated shoals, become clear. Although not depicted in the map here, the subaqueous movement of sediment may be observed as subtle changes of tone representing the dispersion of particles by near-shore waves and currents. Some of the deeper submarine features are also represented. Of particular importance is the depiction of the live reef lying parallel to the Keys in the Atlantic Ocean. The photo not only shows overall distribution of the coral reef but also portrays the geometry of the surge channels and the nature of the channels penetrating into the reef complex. In a few instances, sediment transportation through these channels may also be detected.

Figure 32 is a view of the coast of Camaguey Province in south-central Cuba. The large backreef-lagoon zone dominates this scene. Along the eastern margin the edge of the reef is above sea level, whereas the western margin is completely submerged. There are several pillars in the lagoon-forming islands upon which waves are breaking. Although many shoals can be detected, the lagoon is uniformly shallow with only slight differences in depth. Were it not for high tide, numerous other points would appear as islands, and the shoals would be more effectively delimited. At the Cuban mainland, two lines of breakers can be seen.

This photo emphasizes coastal forms and their areal associations. No other map, chart, or photo can duplicate the water transparency incorporated within the satellite photos. It becomes apparent here, for example, that color tones indicate the continuation of the east-west margin of the coral reef even though the western margin is submerged. The light tones in the lagoons are shallowest and can be correlated with shoals. Both coral pillars and shoals photograph as light tones and show excellent correlation with hydrographic charts.

The Tongue of the Ocean

With increased water turbulence and sediment transport, the color tones would tend to reflect suspended sediment rather than water depth. Therefore, the satellite photos could reflect a multitude of shallow-water phenomena. In this satellite photograph, sediment transport is identifiable only at the river mouths, where the particles are apparently quickly deposited.

Figure 33 shows portions of two major structural features in the Gulf of Mexico: the island of Cuba and the Great Bahama Bank. These and other features are, from the southwest (lower middle) to the northeast (upper right): Cuba, Cayo Romano and shoals, the old Bahama channel, Great Bahama Bank, and the southern edge of the Tongue of the Ocean.

Water over the shoals and Bahama Bank averages 4½ fathoms in depth. The old Bahama channel and Tongue of the Ocean depths are on the order of 600 to 700 fathoms. On this particular photo the various color tones are, to a certain extent, indicative of variations in water depth. A casual glance reveals the contrast between the shallow water over the Great Bahama Bank, the very deep old Bahama channel, and the shoaling offshore reef next to Cuba.

The offshore islands are remnants of a reefal complex now protruding above sea level and dissected into numerous units. Each of the islands is bordered by a shallow-water surface composed of several different elements. On the Atlantic side of the island, the low platform is a narrow zone of recent coral growth. Toward the lagoon, the shallow region is much more extensive and is probably composed of back-reef zones and mud flats. The extremely mottled coloration of this zone suggests contrasts in subaerial and submarine environments as well as between vegetated and nonvegetated zones. The coloration may be complicated by the various types of algal growth that blanket the reef in the intertidal and spray zones.

The waves must have been quite mild when this photo was taken, because lines of breakers are virtually nonexistent, and the lagoon-mainland contact is difficult to discern.

Infrared Imagery

Figure 34 is an infrared image of the Gulf coast of the United States. Gulfport, Miss., is near the center.

The most significant feature of the photograph is the "blooming" effect of the white streaks along the Gulf coast beaches on the island fronting the Gulf of Mexico. The beaches are composed of sand and oyster shells and the spectral response overcomes all other effects.

Recent construction of the Mississippi Gulf Outlet from New Orleans is shown very clearly by the dredging spoil piled up west of the channel. The channel itself, absorbing all infrared reflectance, photographs as a dark line, thus enhancing the light appearance of the spoil banks, caused by reflectance of sand and shells. The narrower beaches on the mainland in the center of the photograph between Bay St. Louis and Biloxi, having more traffic than the island beaches and less shell content, are indicated by less reflectance.

Several areas, such as the shipyards of Pascagoula, show bright splotches on infrared reflectance probably caused by sunlight on metal roofs of buildings.

(*Continued on page 60*)

GEMINI 5   S65–45765

FIGURE 30   Coastal processes are shown in this photo of Laguna de Terminos on Mexico's Yucatan Peninsula.

GEMINI 4   S65–34766

FIGURE 31   This view of the tip of Florida shows features indicated by the map on the facing page.

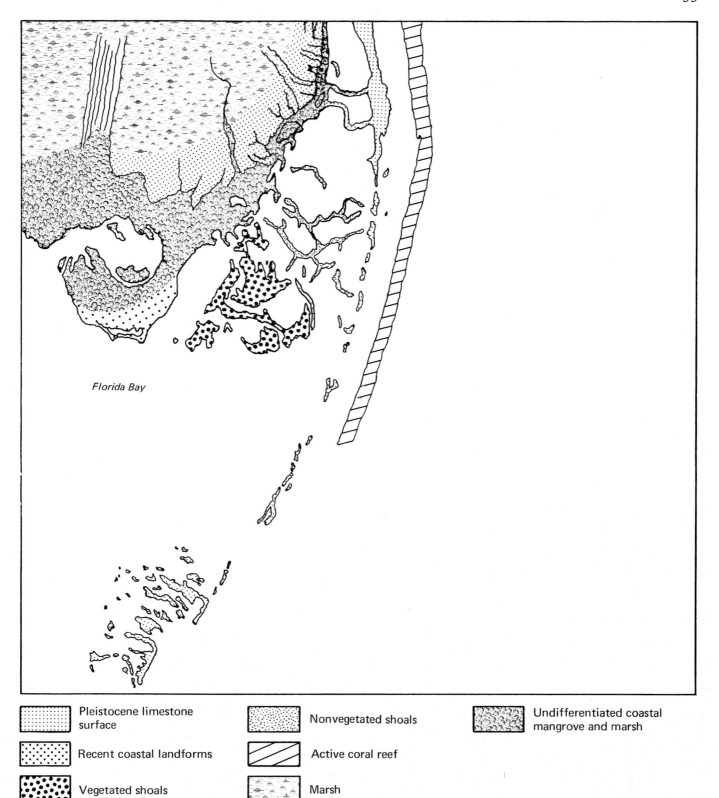

Pleistocene limestone surface

Recent coastal landforms

Vegetated shoals

Nonvegetated shoals

Active coral reef

Marsh

Undifferentiated coastal mangrove and marsh

Florida Bay

FIGURE 31 (Continued)   Some of the variations in the Florida Keys that can be recognized in the photograph.

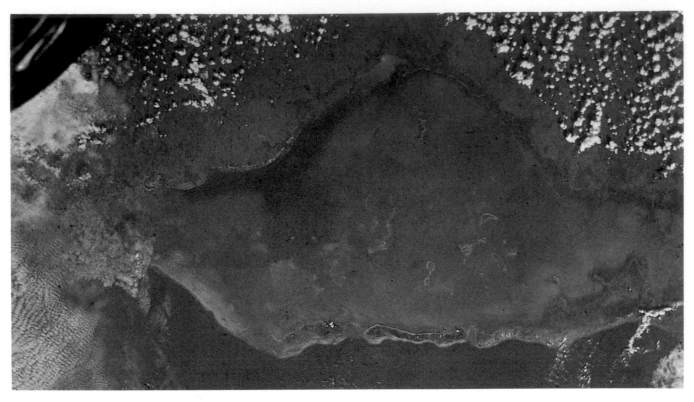

GEMINI 7   S65–64026
FIGURE 32   A large backreef-lagoon (see map below) dominates a satellite photo of Cuba's southern coast.

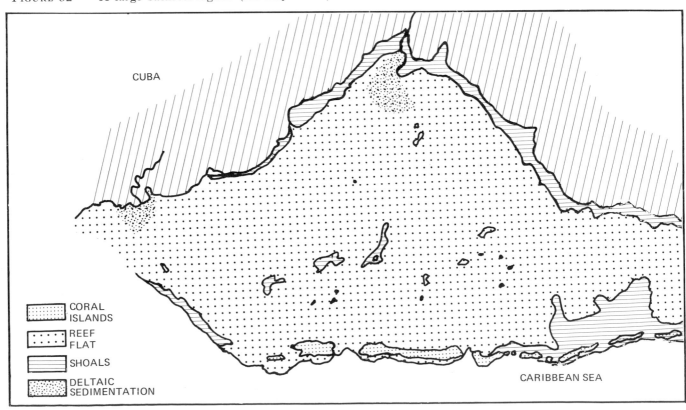

FIGURE 33
A single photo includes
Cuba's northern coast, the
Great Bahama Bank, and
Tongue of the Ocean.

GEMINI 7   S65–64025

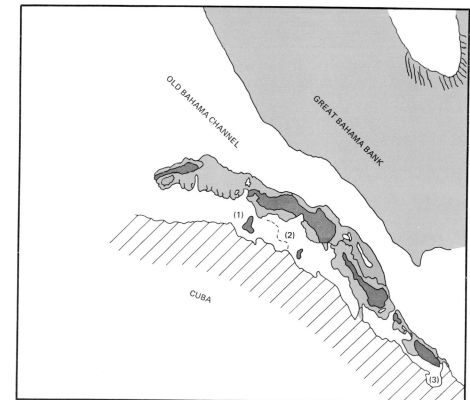

GEMINI 5   S65–64051

FIGURE 34   An infrared picture of 150 miles of the Gulf coast from New Orleans to Gulf State Park, Fla.

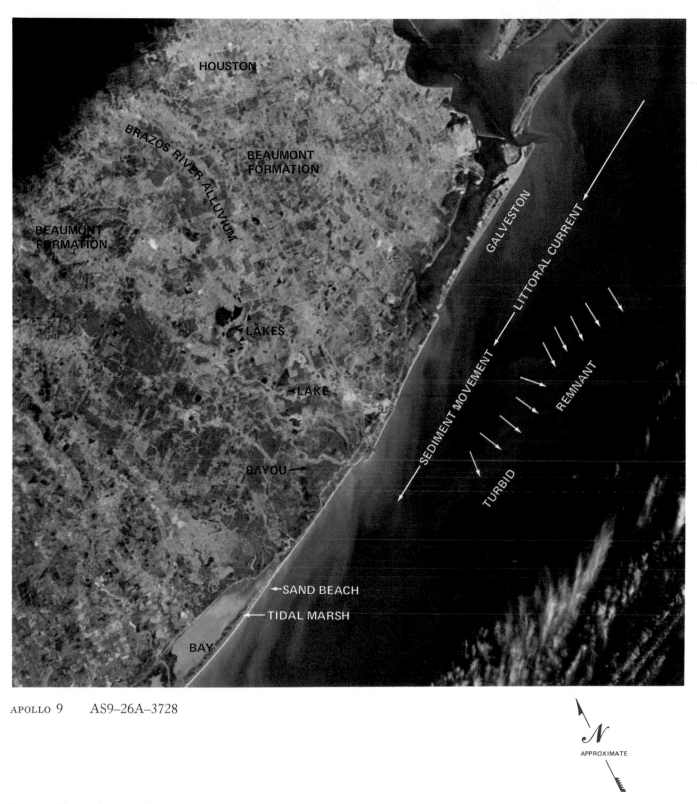

APOLLO 9   AS9–26A–3728

FIGURE 35   A color infrared photo taken by the Apollo 9 astronauts of the Texas coast near Houston.

This photo (fig. 34) gives some indication of the detail on Ektachrome infrared film. Through highways and rivers with white sand banks appear to have great contrast.

Figure 35 is another infrared photo of the Gulf coast of the United States. This one was taken over Houston and Galveston, and conveys much hydrologic and land-use information. The water-related features include the alluvium of the Brazos River, which contains ground water, and numerous lakes, bayous, and bays. The sediment discharge is a good indicator of current movements along the Texas Gulf coast. Light and dark tones in the water of the lakes are indicative of characteristic hydrologic differences.

If satellite surveys of vegetation included the oceans as well as the land surfaces of the globe, much more might be learned about the sea's riches. The worldwide distribution of such readily visible forms as kelp is not known at present. It seems likely, however, that concentrations of such forms of phytoplankton, though invisible to the eye, could be detected by some sensor. The importance of marine ecosystems as determinants of fish populations is enormous; the phytoplankton are known to be differentially distributed, but the actual pattern of distribution is not known. Correlations with other marine phenomena, such as salinity, currents, water temperature, and continental association, might become apparent once the general pattern was established.

Meteorological and other satellites, as well as Gemini and Apollo photography, have suggested many ways in which oceanography can benefit from space science and technology. A seminar on solid-earth and ocean physics, in which more than 65 scientists participated in August 1969, at Williams College, concluded:

If the quality of life is not to decline drastically within 100 years, then we must either limit the population or attain a much more thorough understanding of this Earth on which we live. It is imperative for us to understand the circulation system of the oceans, on which we will depend much more for our food, and the processes in the formation of the Earth crust, from which we tear the materials to build our ever more complex technology.

The attainment of this improved understanding will be a long and difficult task, with some trends we can now predict, but also with many twists and turns we cannot foresee. But we do know that we now have at hand several tools to help mightily in this task: an increasingly accurate and elaborate technology, a ferment of existing ideas in several related areas of geophysical research that are attracting brilliant young people, and a management capability in NASA that could well be turned to matters of social benefit.

Information presented in this chapter was drawn mainly from the work of Norman P. Psuty of the University of Wisconsin; Abraham Anson of the U. S. Army Corps of Engineers; and Robert N. Colwell of the University of California, Berkeley.

CARTOGRAPHY 8

When seen from afar, the Earth's surface often seems to be "a mighty maze," but the elements of a plan may begin to appear when one looks more closely. Until a few centuries ago, few civilized men worshipped nature. Only 50 years ago, schoolboys sometimes debated whether human artists' masterpieces or the products of inanimate forces were more beautiful. Few people took long trips just to see the scenery then. Now that more families can visit remote regions, climb the world's mountains, and descend into its seas, more men have come to appreciate the planet's grandeur. Technology has both increased mankind's dependence on maps and made better cartography attainable.

Transportation Facilities

Figure 36 is a Gemini photograph of western Texas that, in some respects, resembles views of many less populated and less productive parts of the world. This photo can be used, however, to map manmade transportation facilities as well as the rather conspicuous riverbeds. At the far right (1) represents a railroad; all other lines drawn on the photo here represent roads and highways. At (2) a bypass was confirmed by a Texas highway map. The network at (3) was deduced from field boundaries, and (4) might indicate a highway and railroad complex between Odessa and Midland, Tex.

"The potential of extremely high altitudes for revealing transportation data is much greater than anticipated," the interpreter of this photo reported. "With slightly more resolution, contrast, and higher powered lenses than were available to the examiner, it may be that entire road networks in areas such as this could be revealed. There is even a chance that a separation between primary and secondary roads would be possible."

Figure 37 is a Gemini photograph of the border between the United States and Mexico. The valley of the Rio Grande cuts across the picture from the upper left to the bottom center. The Franklin and Organ Mountains are near the center. Below them are El Paso, Tex., and Juarez, Mexico. These cities are in a strategic location in a pass in the range of mountains. There are irrigated areas on both sides of the international borderline. The Rio Grande Valley is slightly depressed and four highways pass through El Paso. The Bison Mountain range contains faults that have provided passages for roads and other means of transportation. The Southern Pacific Railroad uses such a pass. The area is semiarid and is mostly a gravel plain built from the wash of Franklin Mountain. Some of the ranchers have built reservoirs from intermittent streams and graze sheep and cattle.

The nearly vertical Gemini view of this area that is reproduced here was used in two ways: To study the possibilities of using space photography to trace a transportation network, and to examine its usefulness in preparing a physiographic sketch. The interpreters' findings regarding the transportation system are shown in figure 38, and a physiographic sketch of a portion of the photo is presented here as figure 39.

Railroads often can be distinguished from highways by their focus on a major urban center, by gentler curves, and by topographic relationships. In one instance, the width of the image, plus a suggestion of convergence by a highway to the northeast of the urban center, suggested that the highway and the railroad were nearly parallel. Airport runways were somewhat difficult to see, but their position well away from mountains and alinement to the prevailing wind as indicated on a geomorphic overlay seemed to justify the identification of the airport.

Possible extensions of the interpretive rationale, pointed out by a University of Colorado team, were as follows:

It is likely that a relatively dense road network and railroad serves the irrigated districts, but this is not

(*Continued on page 65*)

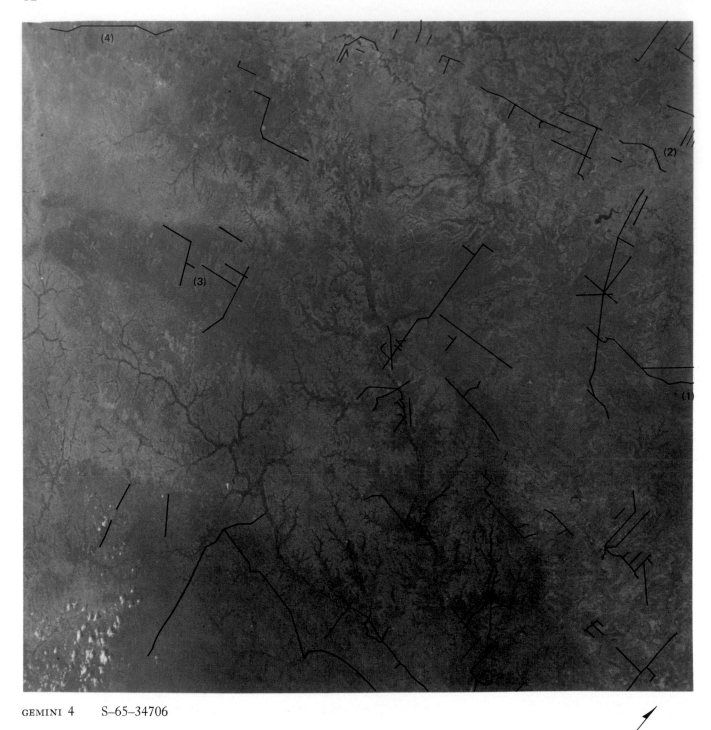

GEMINI 4   S–65–34706

FIGURE 36   A Gemini 4 view of the Edwards Plateau in western Texas, used in a transportation study.

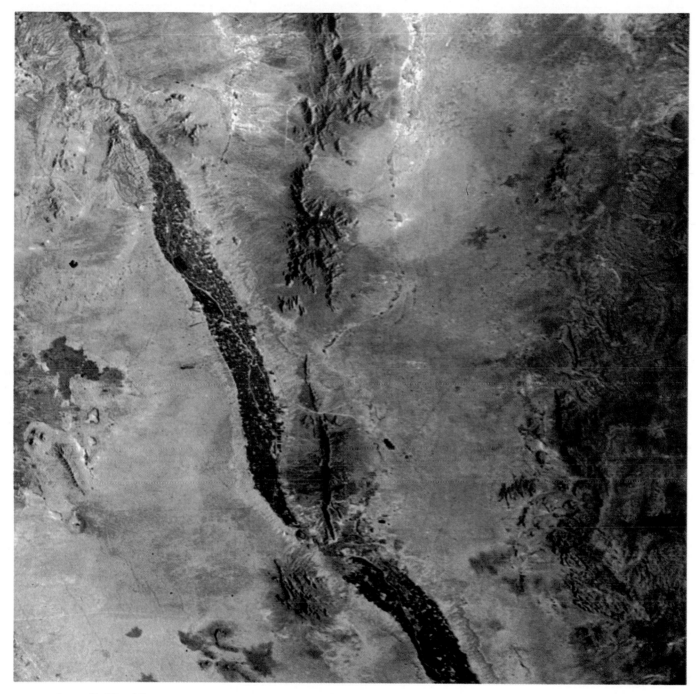

GEMINI 5   S–65–45671

FIGURE 37   A transportation network can be seen in a Gemini photo of the area near El Paso and Juarez.

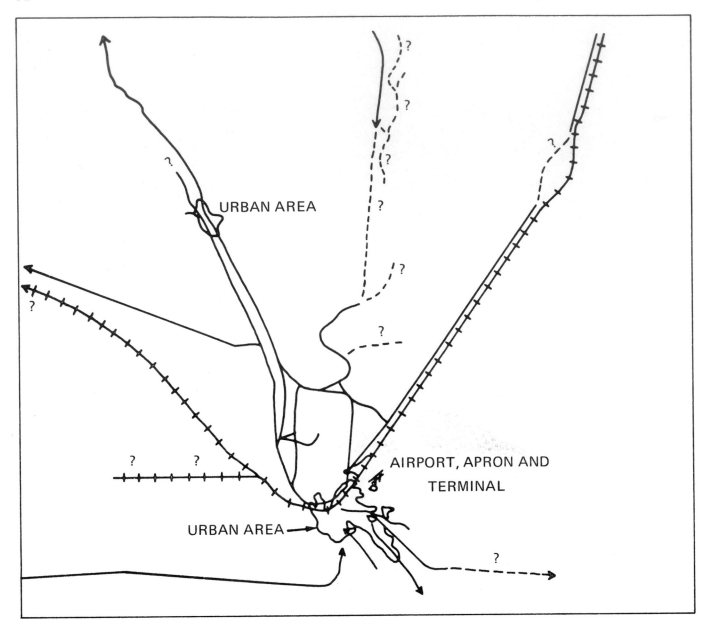

FIGURE 38   An interpreter's map of the transportation network in the photo on the preceding page (fig. 37).

apparent on the space photo. It is reasonable to assume that a major highway exists east of the north-south heading mountains, although only the northern and southern portions are indicated. Relative age of highways serving the northern irrigated districts may be inferred. The old major road is typically situated in the heart of such a district; the newer highway is built on higher ground (terraces) above the valley floor, bypassing the densely settled agricultural land. Highline ditches or canals for irrigation water could be plotted with reasonable accuracy from their division points. These are also evidence of the direction of flow of the main stream.

Techniques of Presentation

Figure 39 is an oblique sketch drawn by Dr. Erwin Raisz of Cambridge, Mass., on brown wrapping paper with pastel crayons. By means of this technique, a large map diagram can be constructed very rapidly and economically. Sketches of this type are often made for briefing or classroom use on paper from 12 to 15 ft long. The paper is inexpensive, readily available, and its color is similar to the surface color of the Earth. By using black, white, and light-colored pastels, a superior relief effect can be presented, especially if a light source is simulated from the right side of the diagram. The Gemini photograph was Dr. Raisz's source material complementary to previous maps.

Figure 40 is one of the many stunning pictures of the Gulf of California taken by the Gemini astronauts. North America's so-called "forgotten peninsula," Baja California, is in the upper left; the large oval there is Bahio Sebastian Viscaino, and the lagoon below it is where the gray whales breed. Dr. Raisz used this space photo to draw the map shown here as figure 41. He had previously produced the most accurate map of this area available for his *Land-*

(*Continued on page 73*)

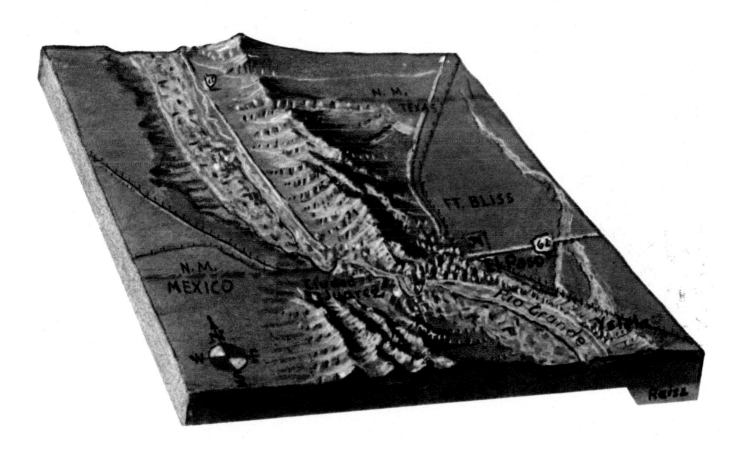

FIGURE 39.   This sketch of a portion of the United States border was drawn from a Gemini photo (fig. 37).

GEMINI 5   S65–45702

FIGURE 40   A Gemini 5 photo of the islands of Angel de la Guarda and Tiburon in the Gulf of California.

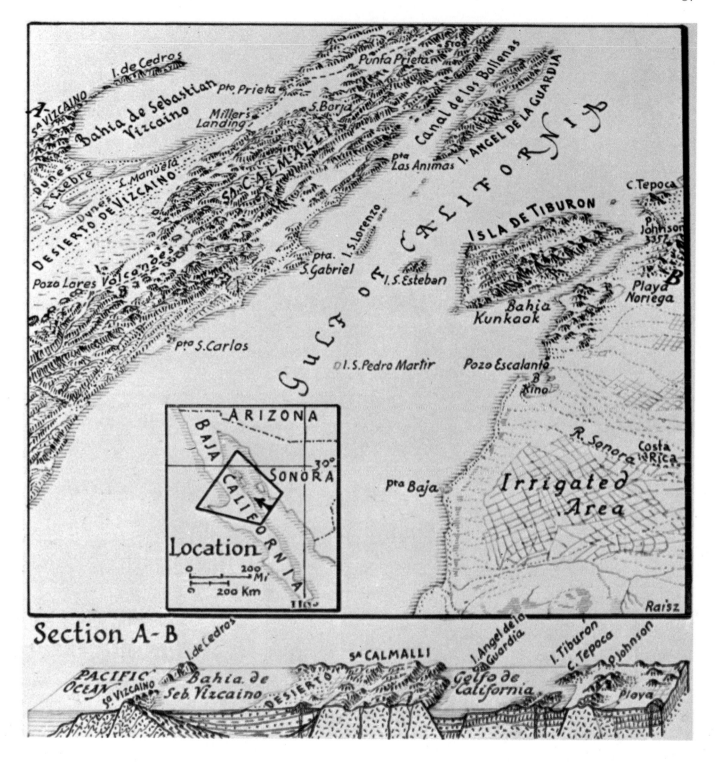

FIGURE 41   A map of the Gulf of California improved by use of information from a Gemini 5 photograph.

GEMINI 5   S65–45599

FIGURE 42   A Gemini 5 photo of Cape Kennedy showed more roads and urban areas than an August 1965 map.

GEMINI 7   S65–63806

FIGURE 43   A Gemini 7 photo of Cape Kennedy in December 1965 showed more changes in urban structure.

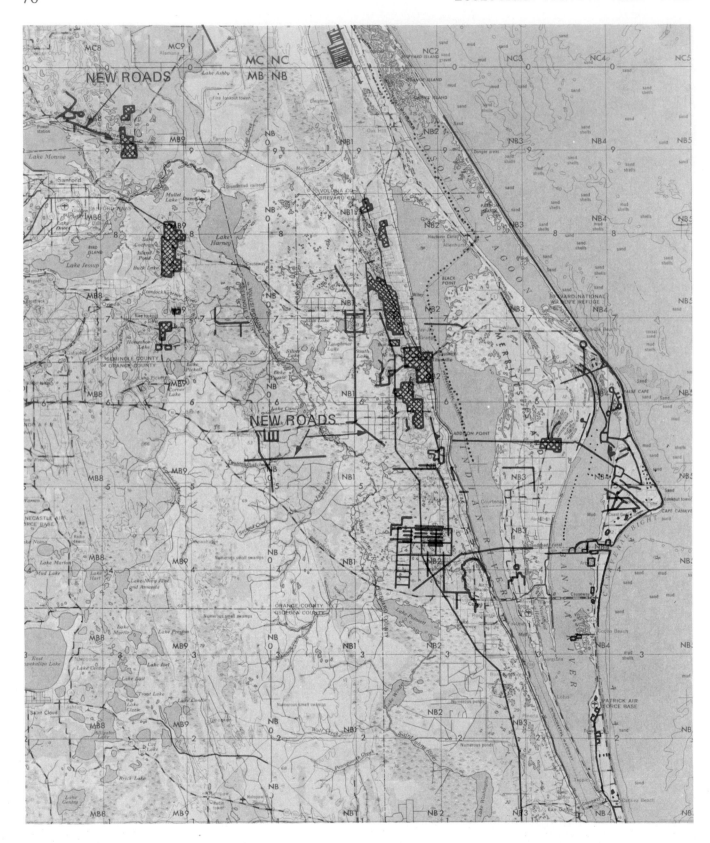

Urban areas

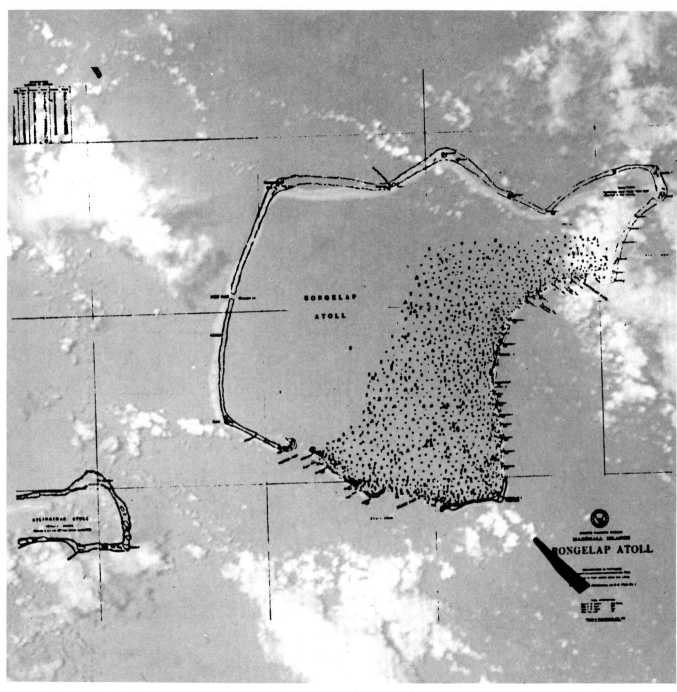

GEMINI 5   S65–45550

ABOVE: FIGURE 45   Matching a Gemini picture of Rongelap atoll
with a hydrographic chart showed differences.

APPROXIMATE

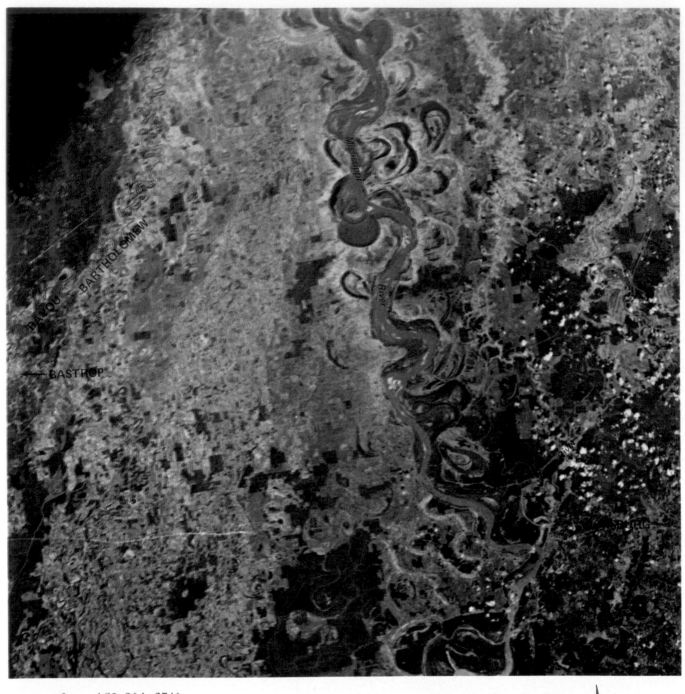

APOLLO 9   AS9–26A–3741

N
APPROXIMATE

FIGURE 46   Recent changes in the Mississippi River become apparent when it is photographed from space.

forms of Mexico. This one shows a larger number of sandy basins, more numerous craters, and the extent of a recently irrigated area that was discernible in the photograph. The mapmaker's use of colored inks makes various features clear that also can be noted when the Gemini photo is examined closely.

So many features of the Earth's surface can be portrayed, and so many of them change so swiftly, that more than 100 000 maps of various types are now being produced annually. Space photos can further increase the accuracy of nearly all kinds of maps and charts, and facilitate the updating that is essential to men's welfare.

Cities and Atolls

The Gemini astronauts demonstrated the value of space photos for swift and accurate updating of maps by photographing the Kennedy Space Center (from which their vehicles had been launched). The resulting photos showed changes that had not been recorded yet by the busy cartographers of that part of Florida.

Figure 42 is a view of Cape Kennedy from a spacecraft over the Florida peninsula in the summer of 1965. This picture clearly shows roads, bridges, and urban areas along that portion of the Atlantic shore. Figure 43 was taken 5 months later, from a different vantage point with a lens of longer focal length, and it revealed additional changes in the urban structure of the region.

Figure 44 is an Army Map Service portrayal of this portion of Florida, to which information derived from the two Gemini flight photos was added afterward. The red lines represent information obtained solely from the Gemini 5 photo, and the blue lines represent information obtained from the Gemini 7 photo.

On the far side of the world from Cape Kennedy, Gemini 5 passed almost directly over Rongelap Atoll in the Marshall Islands of the Pacific and obtained the nearly vertical view used to produce figure 45. This figure shows an existing hydrographic chart (H.O. 6029) reduced and placed over a print of the Gemini photo enlarged to the same scale. Many major features of the atoll are in close alinement with the chart. These are areas that had been well surveyed. There are considerable differences elsewhere, however, between the chart and the photograph because of the inadequacy of the survey prior to the space flight. The rigid geometry of the photo would require that all these features match if the chart were correct. This comparison indicated the areas of improper portrayal that could be readily corrected or verified.

Another atoll, Ailinginae, is in the lower left corner of figure 45. It had been reported to be a half mile from the position given on the chart, but the photo showed that this was not true. The Ailinginae atoll is portrayed in proper relative orientation to Rongelap atoll in this figure. No extensive analysis is necessary to correct a hydrographic chart with a properly taken space photograph; the only effort involved in this case was to adjust the scales of the photo and the chart.

Figure 46 is another Apollo 9 infrared photo. It overlaps figure 13 (chap. 4) and is included here as an illustration of how rapidly the face of the Earth changes. The swirling line from top to bottom is the Mississippi River; Vicksburg is in the lower right quarter of this view, and the photo shows many changes in the river and lake regimen when compared with a 1963 map of this area.

Oxbow lakes and meander scars provide a readily visible record of recent geological history, including the lateral movement of the main channel of the great river. Analysis of these features on repetitive space photography could provide information of direct importance in monitoring changes in the river's regime and in assessing future flood-control requirements. This, in turn, could bear directly on the economy of the whole Mississippi Valley.

Primitive peoples began to draw maps of their parts of the Earth before they learned to write, and often have excelled as cartographers. Aerial photography and electronic surveying have increased the accuracy of many maps and charts in this century, but have not sufficed to keep them up to date. Until quite recently, mapping the whole world on a 1:1 000 000 scale seemed to be almost as ambitious a dream as placing a man on the Moon. Soon much of the Earth will be photographed at that scale. Men's portrayals of the condition, distribution, and depletion of a great many of the Earth's riches then can be made more precise, more vivid, more current, and more useful.

Information for this chapter came largely from the work of Alfred W. Booth of the University of Illinois; Donald D. MacPhail, Albert W. Smith, and Donald E. Vermeer of the University of Colorado; Leo Strees of the U.S. Naval Oceanographic Office; Dr. Erwin Raisz of Cambridge, Mass.; and William D. Carter, William R. Hemphill, and Allan N. Kover of the U. S. Geological Survey.

BIBLIOGRAPHY

Earth Photographs From Gemini III, IV, and V.
NASA SP–129, 1967, 276 pp. GPO $7.

Earth Photographs from Gemini VI Through XII.
NASA SP–171, 1969, 327 pp. GPO $8.

Exploring Space With a Camera.
NASA SP–168, 1968, 214 pp. GPO $4.25.

Gemini Summary Conference.
NASA SP–138, 1967, 345 pp. GPO $2.75.

A Survey of Attitude Sensors for Spacecraft.
NASA SP–145, 1967, 18 pp. CFSTI $3.

Significant Achievements in Space Applications, 1966.
NASA SP–156, 1968, 91 pp. GPO 50 cents.

A Survey of Space Applications.
NASA SP–142, 1967, 135 pp. GPO 70 cents.

☆U.S. Government Printing Office: 1970 O—377-528